Complete SUMMER SMART
Grade 1-2

Special thanks are given to
Vikalp Jain, Dev Patel, Tiffany Feler, Erica Ho,
*and **Marco Chang***
for their involvement in the Arts & Crafts Section.

Printed in China

ISBN: 978-1-897457-96-2

English

Mathematics

Science

Social Studies

Arts & Crafts

Contents

Grade 1-2

Week

ISBN: 978-1-897457-96-2

Safety Rules

Answers

Hands-on Activities

ISBN: 978-1-897457-96-2

Dear Parents,

While all work and no play makes Jack a dull boy, all play and no work would probably make Jack forget most of what he has learned, which is why it is desirable to schedule regular practice in the long summer vacation to help your child consolidate his/her academic skills.

This is where Complete SummerSmart comes in.

Complete SummerSmart is organized in an easy-to-use format: it is made up of eight weeks (units) of work, each comprising consolidation practice in English, Math, Science, and Social Studies, followed by "Arts & Crafts" for developing your child's artistic skills. After practice, your child will be treated to some comics, and he/she will be introduced to a fun place to go in summer, too.

At the end of the book, there is a "Hands-on" section that engages your child in some fun math and language games to consolidate essential skills and concepts.

There is also an answer key for you to check the answers with your child and explain or clarify any items that your child does not understand.

By reviewing the essentials taught in the previous academic year, Complete SummerSmart prepares your child for the grade ahead with confidence.

With Complete SummerSmart, your child will enjoy a fun-filled and meaningful summer break.

Your Partner in Education,
Popular Book Co. (Canada) Ltd.

ISBN: 978-1-897457-96-2

Week 1

English
- read a poem and match rhyming words
- put words in alphabetical order
- learn some new words
- write a paragraph

Mathematics
- draw objects to match numbers
- use position words
- write number words
- read a pictograph

Science
- learn the five senses
- classify animals and plants
- identify living and non-living things

Social Studies
- explore your family tree

Arts & Crafts
- create a picture with your thumb

ISBN: 978-1-897457-96-2

A. Read the poem. Then write the words in bold that rhyme with the given ones.

Summer Fun

The **school** doors **flew** open.

We all rushed out.

It's summer vacation.

We began to shout!

Swimming, biking, playing with **friends**.

Our **days** will be **fun**-filled **till** summer's **end**.

1. sun   fun

2. grew   Flew

3. trays   days

4. fool   school

5. bends   end

6. mill   till

7. send   feinds

8. see   we

 ISBN: 978-1-897457-96-2

B. Read the list of summer activities. Place the words in alphabetical order.

swimming

soccer

biking

hiking

baseball

tennis

fishing

rollerblading

camping

boating

1. _____

2. _____

3. _____

4. _____

5. _____

6. _____

7. _____

8. _____

9. _____

10. _____

ISBN: 978-1-897457-96-2

C. Circle the words from (B) in the word search.

b	u	s	s	o	c	c	e	r	g	s	r
i	e	t	w	j	l	r	c	l	e	m	o
k	h	f	i	s	h	i	n	g	p	q	l
i	g	j	m	b	a	s	e	b	a	l	l
n	i	o	m	v	i	p	a	l	r	s	e
g	q	i	i	e	j	o	s	c	h	s	r
t	e	n	n	i	s	u	d	a	z	d	b
p	k	v	g	l	e	y	f	m	x	f	l
r	h	s	e	p	q	t	g	p	c	g	a
t	f	t	u	t	a	r	j	i	v	y	d
h	i	k	i	n	g	e	k	n	b	k	i
y	w	k	s	o	c	w	l	g	n	o	n
c	d	b	o	a	t	i	n	g	m	v	g

ISBN: 978-1-897457-96-2

D. Read the paragraph and write a paragraph about something that you enjoy doing during the summer. Draw a picture to go with your paragraph.

A paragraph is a group of sentences about one main idea.

I enjoy biking. It is good exercise. I can look at the trees, flowers, and birds along the way. Maybe this summer, I will see some interesting animals too.

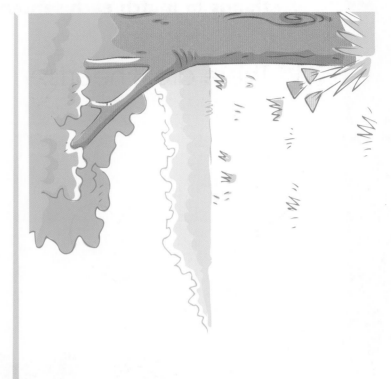

My Paragraph

ISBN: 978-1-897457-96-2

9

A. Fiona and Mary are drawing. Help them draw more things to match each sentence.

1. There are 3 hearts.

2. There are 5 cups.

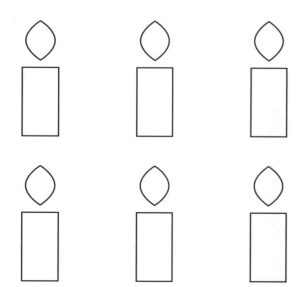

3. There are 10 candles.

ISBN: 978-1-897457-96-2

B. Circle the correct words.

1. The girl is   in / behind   the boy.

2. The girl is   in front of / behind   the table.

3. The green coat is   behind / on   the pink coat.

4. The pair of scissors is   on / under   the desk.

5. The crown is   above / beside   the boy's head.

6. The two pieces of paper are   under / above   the roll of tape.

C. Look at Fiona's picture. Do the colouring and fill in the number words.

1. There are _____ apples in all.

2. _____ apples are on the ground.

3. _____ ducks are on the grass.

4. _____ rabbits are hopping.

5. There are _____ rabbits in all.

6. There is _____ cat.

7. _____ monkeys are in the tree.

ISBN: 978-1-897457-96-2

D. **Read the pictograph that shows the drawing tools Fiona has. Then answer the questions.**

Fiona's Drawing Tools

1. Do the recording.

Kind of Tool	Number of Tools
crayon	
paintbrush	
paint	

2. How many more crayons than paintbrushes does Fiona have?

   _____ more

3. How many kinds of tools does Fiona have?

   _____

ISBN: 978-1-897457-96-2

A. We have five senses. Draw lines to match the objects with the senses.

- hearing

- smell

- touch

- taste

- sight

Many bats are nearly blind. They use their sense of hearing to "see"!

Science

ISBN: 978-1-897457-96-2

B. Complete the poems by using "sense" words.

Is it mashed potatoes,
Porridge or paste?
I know it by

My Sense of

1. _____

There! In the sky!
A plane or a kite?
I know it by

My Sense of

2. _____

Skunk or flower?
It's easy to tell.
I know it by

My Sense of

3. _____

A haircut. What's left?
I say, "Not much!"
I know it by

My Sense of

4. _____

The band is playing,
The crowd is cheering.
I know it by

My Sense of

5. _____

ISBN: 978-1-897457-96-2

C. Label each living thing as an animal or a plant.

1.

2.

3.

4.

5.

ISBN: 978-1-897457-96-2

D. Identify each thing as living or non-living.

1.  _____

2.  _____

3.  _____

4.  _____

5.

6.

7.

ISBN: 978-1-897457-96-2

A family tree shows the members in your family. Write who's who in your family in the tree below. Ask an adult if you need help.

Social Studies

| Grandfather | Grandmother |

| Father |

Me

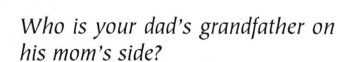

Who is your dad's grandfather on his mom's side?

1. _____

ISBN: 978-1-897457-96-2

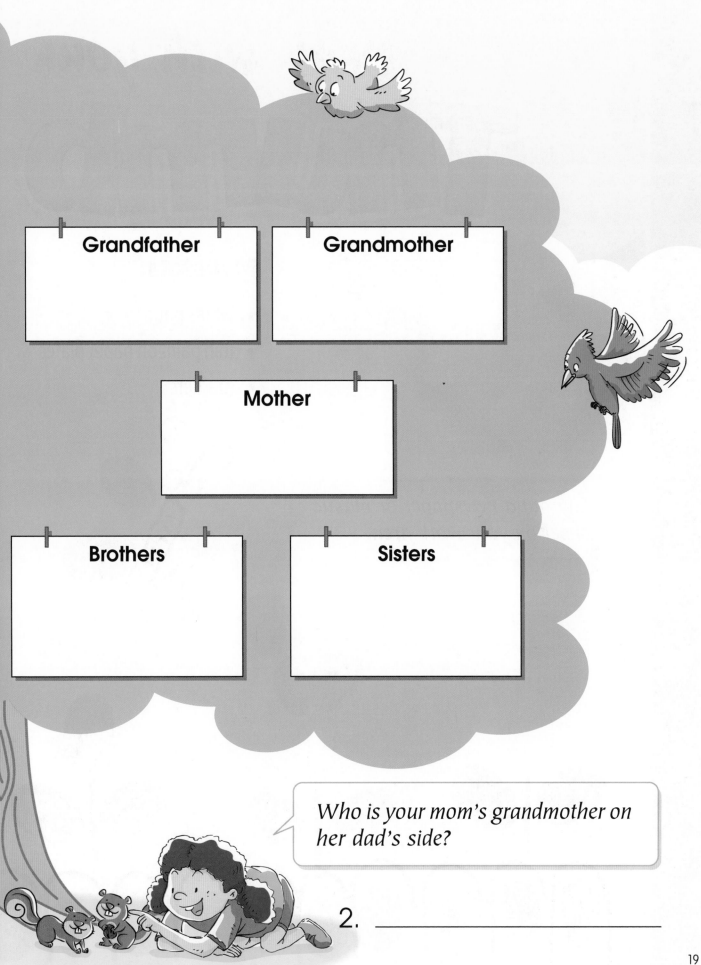

Grandfather

Grandmother

Mother

Brothers

Sisters

Who is your mom's grandmother on her dad's side?

2. _____

ISBN: 978-1-897457-96-2

Draw with your Thumb

Materials:

- white paper
- thin paint on paper plates
- markers

> Lay out a newspaper or plastic sheet on your work area.

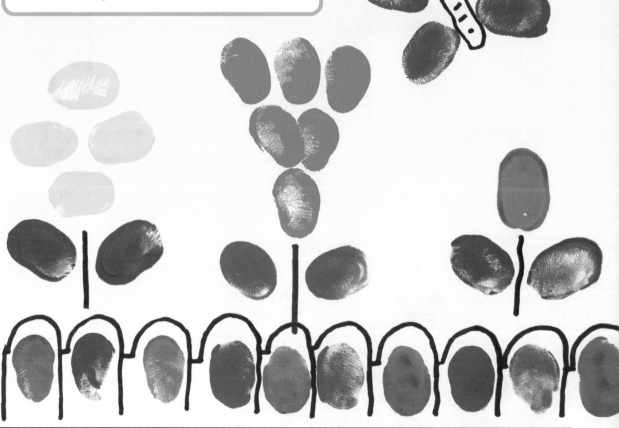

ISBN: 978-1-897457-96-2

Directions:

1. Pour about 1 tablespoon of dry paint onto each paper plate.

2. Pour about 1 tablespoon of water onto paint and mix.

3. Press your thumb onto paint. Wipe off excess.

4. "Draw" a picture.

5. Add details with markers.

ISBN: 978-1-897457-96-2

COMICS

An **Adventurous** *Day at the Beach*

Part 1

Leo, Jack, and Ann were at the beach on a sunny day.

They bought ice cream, but a seagull snatched Ann's away.

Why mine?

Ahh...

Then, while Leo was trying to catch a crab, it nipped his finger.

ISBN: 978-1-897457-96-2

ISBN: 978-1-897457-96-2

Grade 1-2

The **ZOO** – *Where We Meet Wild Animals*

The zoo is home to many animals. It is a great place to spend a hot summer day.

When we visit the animals, we should treat them with courtesy. We should not make loud noises because that may scare them. And for our own safety, we should not climb fences, feed animals, or pick plants.

While at the zoo, we can watch how different animals live and play. Sometimes, we may have a chance to see them do things that we do not think they can do. We can even draw a picture of the animal that we like best and give it a name.

The zoo is a fun place to go.

ISBN: 978-1-897457-96-2

WEEK 2

Week **2**

English
- read a sign and answer questions
- categorize words
- add punctuation marks to sentences
- correct wrong consonants

Mathematics
- do counting
- recognize patterns and find probabilities
- read a pictograph
- estimate amounts

Science
- know the basic needs of living things
- categorize food items by type
- recognize healthy food items
- learn the parts of a plant

Social Studies
- write personal information
- draw and write your favourite items

Arts & Crafts
- make symmetrical cut-outs

ISBN: 978-1-897457-96-2

A. Read the sign. Then give short answers to the questions.

GARAGE SALE

Date: Saturday, July 1
Sunday, July 2

Time: 9:00 a.m. to 3:00 p.m.

Items: toys, clothes, furniture, comic books

1. What time does the garage sale begin?

_____

2. What time does the garage sale end?

_____

3. On which days will the sale be held?

_____

4. What kinds of things can you buy at the garage sale?

_____

English

ISBN: 978-1-897457-96-2

B. **Here is a list of things sold at the garage sale. Read the list and put each word or phrase in the correct box.**

Garage Sale

pants   chair   coat   dress   hat

doll   desk   teddy bear   couch

scarf   table   baseball   skipping rope

bed   jigsaw puzzle

Furniture

_____

_____

_____

_____

Clothing

_____

_____

_____

_____

Toy

_____

_____

_____

_____

ISBN: 978-1-897457-96-2

1.

I like the skipping rope ☐

You can have it for a dollar ☐

2.

Can I take it home ☐

Of course ☐

3.

Be careful ☐

ISBN: 978-1-897457-96-2

D. Look at each picture and read the words. One consonant is wrong. Correct and rewrite each word.

puck
_ _ _ _

pat
_ _ _

cut
_ _ _

look
_ _ _ _

ramp
_ _ _ _

big
_ _ _

bite
_ _ _ _

fun
_ _ _

fair
_ _ _ _

hike
_ _ _ _

29

ISBN: 978-1-897457-96-2

A. Look at Lucy's marbles. Fill in the blanks.

1. **Lucy has**...

   • _____

   • _____

   • _____ marbles in all.

   • _____ types of marbles.

2. If the value of each marble is 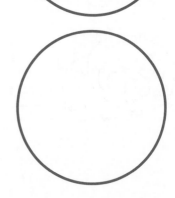, the value of all the marbles that Lucy has is _____ cents.

3. If 4 of the marbles in the tube glow in the dark, _____ marbles do not glow in the dark.

4. Draw the pattern of the first marble that Lucy put in the tube.

5. Draw the pattern of the sixth marble that Lucy put in the tube.

ISBN: 978-1-897457-96-2

B. Ivy also has some marbles. Answer the questions and check ✔ the correct answers.

1. How many 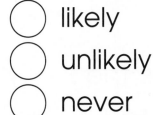 does Ivy have?   _____

2. How many marbles does she have in all?   _____

3. How many marbles are between the 3rd marble and the 7th?   _____

4. If Ivy puts in another marble following the pattern, will the marble be green or purple?   _____

5. Ivy puts all her marbles into a box and picks one out. What is the chance that she will

   a. pick a 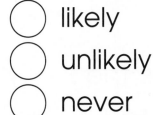 ?

      ◯ likely
      ◯ unlikely
      ◯ never

   b. pick a  ?

      ◯ likely
      ◯ unlikely
      ◯ never

ISBN: 978-1-897457-96-2

C. **Look at the graph. Answer the questions. Write the numbers or draw the patterns.**

Number of Marbles Tina has

1. How many does Tina have?   _____

2. How many ～ does Tina have?   _____

3. How many types of marbles does Tina have?   _____

4. How many marbles does Tina have in all?   _____

5. Which type of marble does Tina have the most of?   ◯

6. Which type of marble does Tina have the fewest of?   ◯

7. Which type of marble is the same number as that of 🌼 ?   ◯

ISBN: 978-1-897457-96-2

D. Chris puts every 10 marbles into a bag. Help him estimate how many marbles are in each group. Write "fewer" or "more" on the lines. Then do the counting and write the total.

1.

Estimate:

_____ than 40

Exact:

_____

2.

Estimate:

_____ than 30

Exact:

_____

3.

Estimate:

_____ than 20

Exact:

_____

ISBN: 978-1-897457-96-2

Grade 1-2

A. Fill in the blanks to complete what the children say.

> warmth   food   air   water

All living things need 1. _____ .

All living things need 2. _____ .

Basic Needs
of **Living Things**

All living things need 3. _____ .

All living things need 4. _____ .

ISBN: 978-1-897457-96-2

B. Draw a line to match each food item with the plant or animal from which it comes.

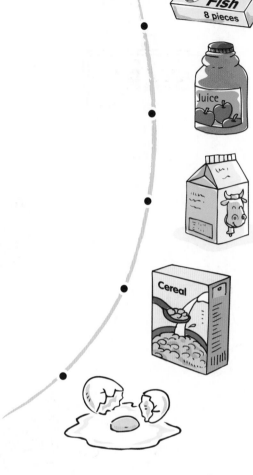

cow　　•

corn　　•

fish　　•

chicken　•

apple tree　•

C. Put each food item in the correct cart.

A. puffed rice　B. fish　C. bread　D. broccoli
E. cheese　　　F. milk　G. egg　H. orange

Grain　　Fruit and Vegetables　　Dairy　　Meat and Alternatives

ISBN: 978-1-897457-96-2　　*Grade 1-2*

D. **Complete the maze by choosing good food items to eat for breakfast. Then write the good food items on the lines.**

- _____

- _____

- _____

- _____

Science Fun

Blue whales eat about 4000 kilograms of krill each day.

ISBN: 978-1-897457-96-2

E. **Label the parts of the plant. Then do the matching.**

Parts of a Plant

flower   stem   leaf   roots

- holds the leaves up and transports water

- makes seeds

- makes food

- hold the plant in place and get water

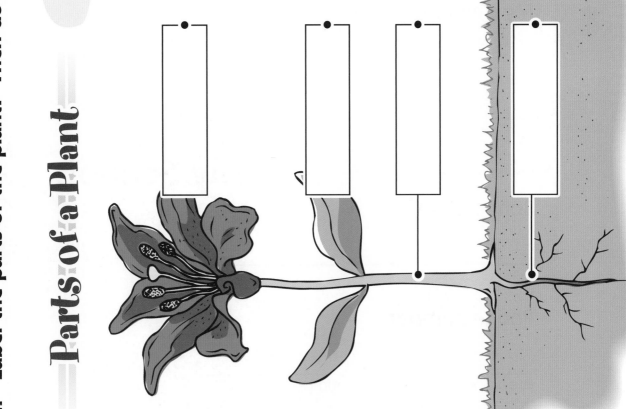

37

ISBN: 978-1-897457-96-2

A. Fill in your personal information. You may ask an adult to help you.

Personal information includes where you live, your telephone number, and other things about you. You should never disclose your personal information to a stranger.

My Home

My address:

_____ _____
number   street

_____ _____ _____
city   province/territory   postal code

My phone number:

_____ _____
area code   number

My School

School name:

_____

Phone number:

_____ _____
area code   number

ISBN: 978-1-897457-96-2

B. Glue your picture. Then draw and write your favourite items.

My Picture

Glue your picture here.

My
Favourite

Food

Drink

Animal

ISBN: 978-1-897457-96-2

Materials:

• construction paper

• scissors

• pencil

Symmetrical Cut-outs

ISBN: 978-1-897457-96-2

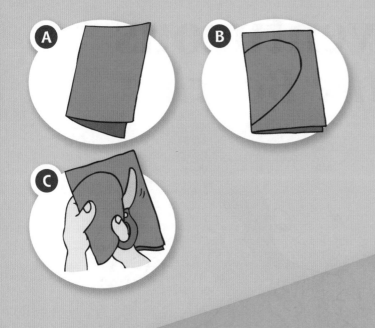

Directions:

1. Fold a piece of construction paper in half.

2. Draw like Diagram B.

3. Cut out the shape.

4. Unfold the cut-out.

5. What do you get?

Now use another piece of paper and make a symmetrical cut-out of your own.

ISBN: 978-1-897457-96-2

An **Adventurous** Day at the Beach

Part 2

The children found a chest. They opened it. It was filled with treasure.

We found treasure!

It's all right.

Haha...

Then they saw some pirates come towards them. The children had nowhere to hide.

The pirates laughed and told them that they were just filming a movie.

ISBN: 978-1-897457-96-2

When the filming was over, the pirates gave the children the "treasure".

They let the children stay and watch.

What an adventure!

It was sunny again with a beautiful rainbow across the sky. The children left the cave with their new "treasure".

/// **The End**

43

ISBN: 978-1-897457-96-2

Grade 1-2

The Pick-Your-Own Farm

Summer is the time when many types of fruit, like cherries and peaches, and vegetables, like tomatoes and sweet corn, come into season. Yes, you can get them from local markets, but picking your own fruit and vegetables fresh from the farm can be more fun than you can imagine.

Fresh fruit and vegetables are not only yummy but also good for your health. At a pick-your-own farm, you can eat the fruit right on the spot or take the fresh vegetables home.

While you enjoy picking fruit and vegetables in the sun, don't forget to wear a cap and apply sunscreen! Also, wash your "pick" with clean water before eating!

ISBN: 978-1-897457-96-2

WEEK 3

English

- read a story and answer questions
- put sentences in order
- learn compound words
- solve riddles

Mathematics

- do counting
- find total value of coins
- identify symmetrical figures
- read a pictograph

Science

- learn where animals build their homes
- learn the life cycles of different animals

Social Studies

- put events in order on a timeline
- find out more about your best friend

Arts & Crafts

- make a picture using handprints

ISBN: 978-1-897457-96-2

A. Read the story. Then give short answers to the questions.

Bob's
Bird Bath

Bob was so excited. He found a treasure at his neighbour's garage sale. It was an old bird bath. It cost only $1. Bob bought the bird bath and placed it outside in his backyard. He then took the garden hose and filled the bath with water. As the afternoon sun warmed the water, Bob watched robins, bluebirds, and cardinals enjoy the bird bath.

1. Where did Bob get the bird bath?

_____

2. How much was the bird bath?

_____

3. Where did Bob put his bird bath?

_____

4. What kinds of birds visited Bob's bird bath?

_____

ISBN: 978-1-897457-96-2

B. Read the five sentences. Rewrite them in the correct order.

- Bob bought the bird bath.
- The sun warmed the water.
- Bob found a treasure.
- He filled the bath with water.
- Bob put the bird bath in the backyard.

1. _____

2. _____

3. _____

4. _____

5. _____

C. Read the story again. Find four compound words and write them on the lines below.

1. _____

2. _____

3. _____

4. _____

ISBN: 978-1-897457-96-2

D. Complete the compound words.

paper	fish	melon	board
cake	box	ball	fly

news _____

pan _____

mail _____

gold _____

foot _____

water _____

butter _____

cup _____

ISBN: 978-1-897457-96-2

E. Use the code to solve the riddles.

Secret Code

A	B	C	D	E	F	G	H	I	J	K	L	M
1	2	3	4	5	6	7	8	9	10	11	12	13

N	O	P	Q	R	S	T	U	V	W	X	Y	Z
14	15	16	17	18	19	20	21	22	23	24	25	26

1.

What bird is always at the dining table?

$\overline{}_{1} \quad \overline{}_{19} \; \overline{}_{23} \; \overline{}_{1} \; \overline{}_{12} \; \overline{}_{12} \; \overline{}_{15} \; \overline{}_{23}$

2.

What does a duck eat with its soup?

$\overline{}_{3} \; \overline{}_{18} \; \overline{}_{1} \; \overline{}_{3} \; \overline{}_{11} \; \overline{}_{5} \; \overline{}_{18} \; \overline{}_{19}$

3. What bird is always sad?

$\overline{}_{1} \quad \overline{}_{2} \; \overline{}_{12} \; \overline{}_{21} \; \overline{}_{5} \; \overline{}_{2} \; \overline{}_{9} \; \overline{}_{18} \; \overline{}_{4}$

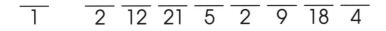

49

ISBN: 978-1-897457-96-2

A. Count and write how many things are in each group. Then fill in the blanks.

1.

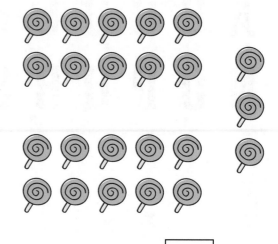

Group A: ☐   Group B: ☐

Group _____ is easier to count.

2.

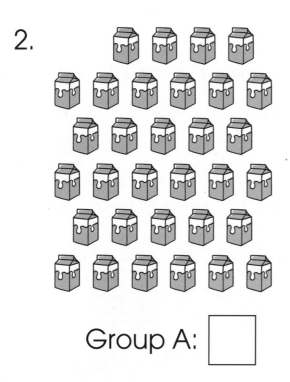   

Group A: ☐   Group B: ☐

Group _____ is easier to count.

ISBN: 978-1-897457-96-2

B. Gary shows the cost of each item with coins. Write the costs. Then solve the problems.

1.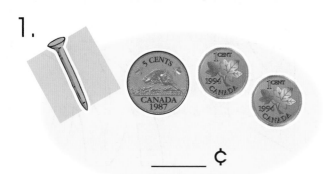

_____ ¢

2.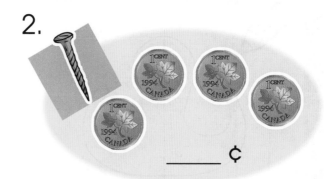

_____ ¢

3.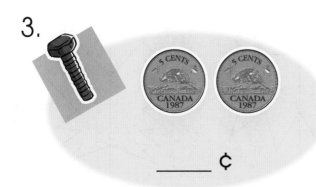

_____ ¢

4.

_____ ¢

5. 1 hinge needs 6 screws. How many screws are needed for 2 hinges?

_____ = _____

_____ screws are needed.

6. Gary has 7 nails in the drawer and 8 nails in the box. How many nails does he have in all?

_____ = _____

He has _____ nails in all.

ISBN: 978-1-897457-96-2

C. Colour the logos that are symmetrical.

Week

3

D. Put the pictures in order. Write 1, 2, 3, and 4.

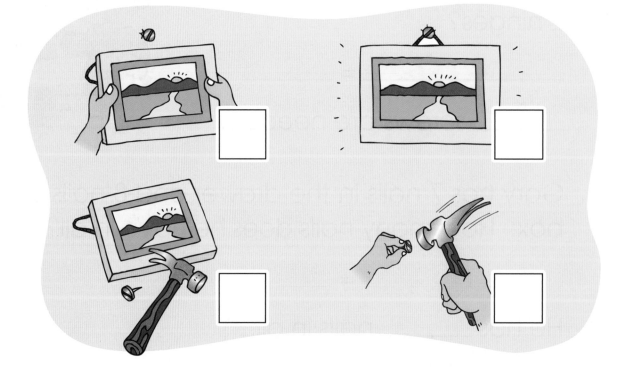

ISBN: 978-1-897457-96-2

E. Gary uses a graph to show how many photos he took last week. Look at the graph. Then fill in the blanks.

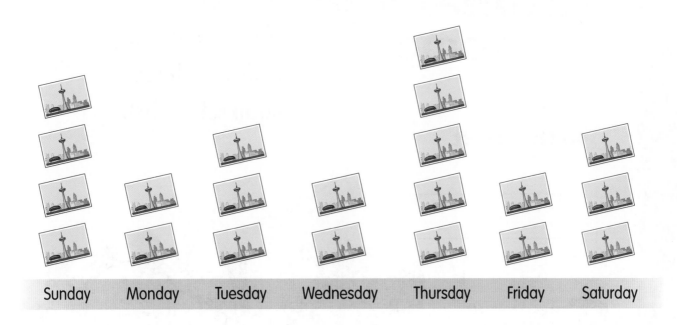

Number of Photos Taken Last Week

Sunday   Monday   Tuesday   Wednesday   Thursday   Friday   Saturday

1. On Wednesday, Gary took _____ photos.

2. From Monday to Friday, Gary took _____ photos in all.

3. Gary took 4 photos on _____ .

4. Gary took the most photos on _____ .

5. Gary took _____ more photos on Thursday than he did on Wednesday.

6. Gary took _____ photos in all.

53

ISBN: 978-1-897457-96-2

A. Where do these animals make their homes? Write the names of the animals in the environment in which they live.

Animal Homes

fox   shrimp

bird   bear

squirrel   fish

In the forest

_____

_____

In the river

_____

_____

In the tree

_____

_____

ISBN: 978-1-897457-96-2

B. Draw a line to lead each animal to its home.

ISBN: 978-1-897457-96-2

C. **We have special names for different animals' homes. Use the clues to complete the puzzle with the given words.**

Sometimes animals make their homes in other animals' homes. Hermit crabs look for empty shells. A cuckoo bird lays her eggs in other birds' nests.

NEST   DEN   LODGE   WEB   HIVE   SHELL

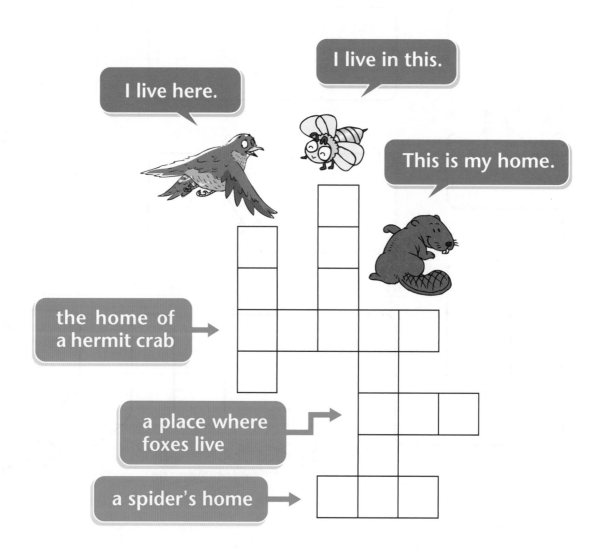

I live here.

I live in this.

This is my home.

the home of a hermit crab →

a place where foxes live →

a spider's home →

ISBN: 978-1-897457-96-2

D. Label the stages of each animal's life cycle.

1.

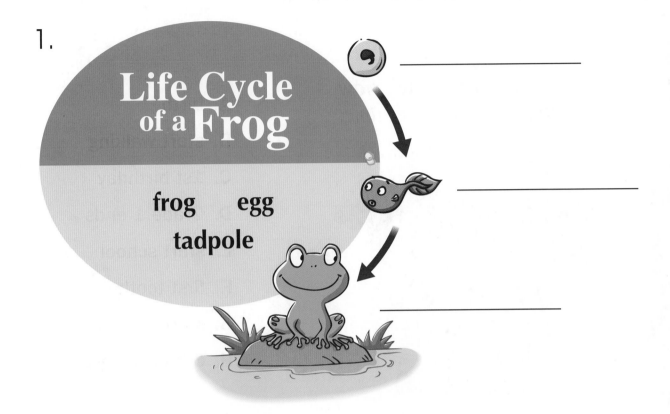

Life Cycle of a **Frog**

frog   egg
tadpole

_____

_____

_____

2.

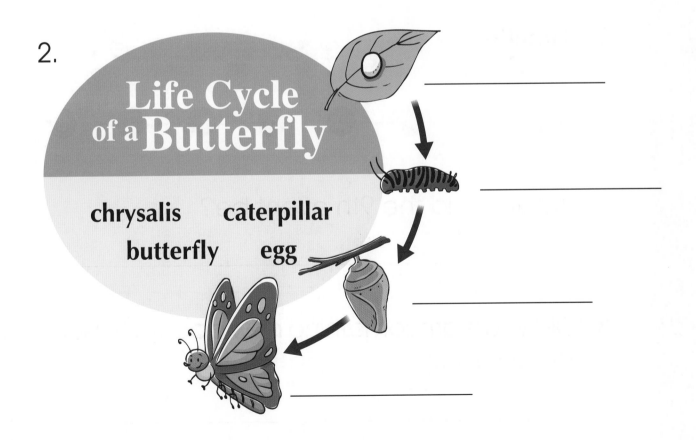

Life Cycle of a **Butterfly**

chrysalis   caterpillar
butterfly   egg

_____

_____

_____

_____

57

ISBN: 978-1-897457-96-2

A. Read the events from your life. Write the letters in the correct spaces on the timeline.

Events from Your Life

A. birth

B. start walking

C. 1st birthday

D. Grade 1 ends

E. start school

F. first tooth

G. start talking

H. 6th birthday

A timeline shows how things change over time.

1. **Timeline**

2. What could the 9th event be?

_____

3. Did you learn something new about yourself? What was it?

_____

_____

ISBN: 978-1-897457-96-2

B. **Fill in the information about your best friend. Then draw a picture of you and your best friend.**

All about **My Best Friend**

His/Her name: _____

His/Her age: _____

His/Her birthday: _____

He/She lives near me: Yes / No

We go to the same school: Yes / No

My Best Friend and I

ISBN: 978-1-897457-96-2

Materials:

- crayons or coloured pencils
- paper
- pencil

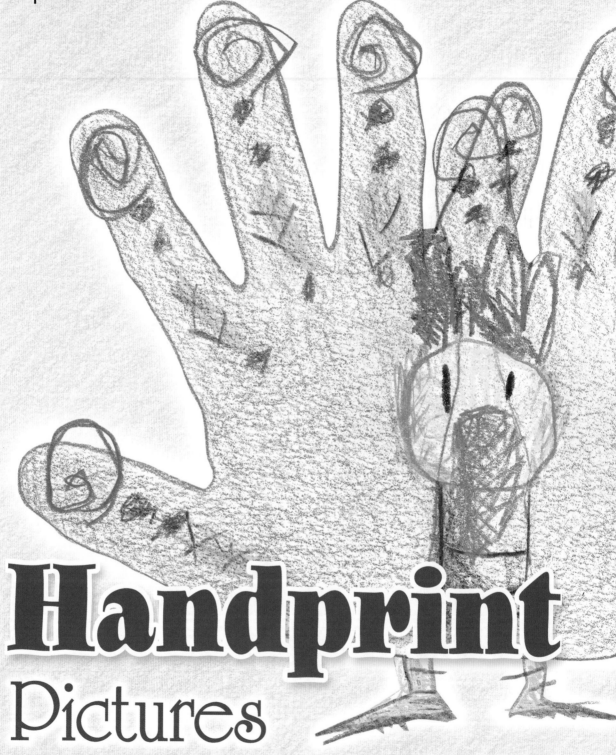

Handprint
Pictures

ISBN: 978-1-897457-96-2

You can trace both hands side by side or overlap for interesting results.

Directions:

1. Place your hand on a piece of blank paper.
2. Trace the outline of your hand.
3. Add squiggles and create a masterpiece!

ISBN: 978-1-897457-96-2

The Mouse-Deer's Trick

Part 1

Once there was an old tiger.
He lived in a big forest.

Every day, he would try to catch other animals by the salt lick.

The other animals were troubled.
They needed salt to stay healthy.

This is bad.

62

ISBN: 978-1-897457-96-2

Among the animals was a wise mouse-deer.

Don't worry. I have a plan.

The mouse-deer went to see the tiger.

Mr. Tiger, do you want me to bring you food?

Yes.

Then, the mouse-deer went to see the flying squirrel.

Will you help me?

The flying squirrel was brave. She agreed to help the mouse-deer and the other animals.

Let's do it!

To be continued...

ISBN: 978-1-897457-96-2

Grade 1-2

The Petting Farm

Visiting a petting farm can make your summer fun and educational.

At a petting farm, you will see farm animals, like pigs, cows, goats, horses, and chickens. If you are lucky, you may see some newborn baby animals too! Petting farms usually have tour guides who will take you around the farm and tell you interesting facts about each animal. You may get the chance to feed, pet, or even groom some of the animals, but don't forget to wash your hands after direct contact with them. At some petting farms, farmers will show you how to milk a cow or shear a sheep. You can also enjoy a pony ride or a hayride.

Spending a day at a petting farm is a great summer experience.

64

ISBN: 978-1-897457-96-2

WEEK 4

Week 4

English
- complete a story
- find sentences that do not belong
- write sentences
- recognize consonant blends

Mathematics
- name shapes
- do counting
- draw shapes
- learn comparative words

Science
- identify the shapes of structures
- identify natural and human-made structures
- learn the homes of animals
- learn the functions of structures

Social Studies
- put daily events in order
- describe some special events

Arts & Crafts
- play a scribble game

ISBN: 978-1-897457-96-2

A. Read the story. Then fill in the blanks with the words in the word bank.

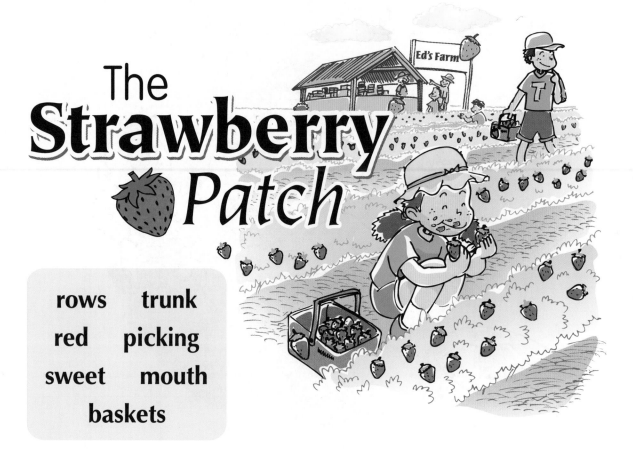

The Strawberry Patch

rows   trunk
red   picking
sweet   mouth
baskets

Jan, Ted, and Aunt Mary were going strawberry 1._____ . They put four empty 2._____ into the 3._____ of the car and left for the strawberry patch.

The children were thrilled when they saw the 4._____ of strawberries. Jan picked one big, 5._____ berry and popped it into her 6._____ . It was so very juicy and 7._____ .

ISBN: 978-1-897457-96-2

B. Read each group of sentences. Draw a line through the sentence that does not belong.

1. The patch was covered with strawberries. Jan picked two baskets of strawberries. There was a robin in the sky.

2. Strawberry picking is fun. Jan and Ted enjoy riding their bikes with Aunt Mary. You can eat as you pick.

3. I like strawberries. They taste sweet and they smell good. We can make strawberry jam too. Grapes are purple in colour.

4. The strawberry patch was up north. Cherries are red too. It took us two hours to drive there.

5. I can make baskets. Ted's basket is very big. He fills it with strawberries.

ISBN: 978-1-897457-96-2

C. **Decorate the welcome sign for the farm. Then write three sentences about the children and Aunt Mary's trip to the farm.**

_____

_____

_____

_____

ISBN: 978-1-897457-96-2

D. Say what each picture is. Circle the consonant blend the word
   has. Then write the word on the line.

> skates   flower   grapes   clown
> plane   star   flag   spider

1. **sl sk sp**

_____

2.

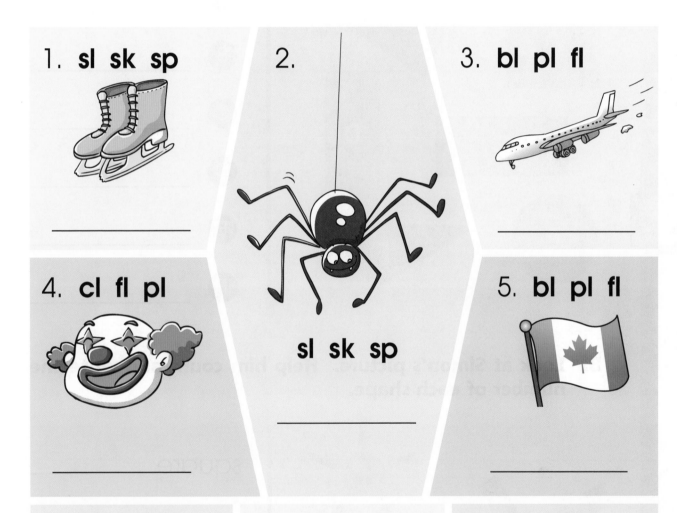

sl sk sp

_____

3. **bl pl fl**

_____

4. **cl fl pl**

_____

5. **bl pl fl**

_____

6. **gr gl cl**

_____

7. **bl pl fl**

_____

8. **st sp cl**

_____

ISBN: 978-1-897457-96-2

A. Simon has cut out some shapes from a cardboard. Help him name the shapes.

> circle   triangle   rectangle   square

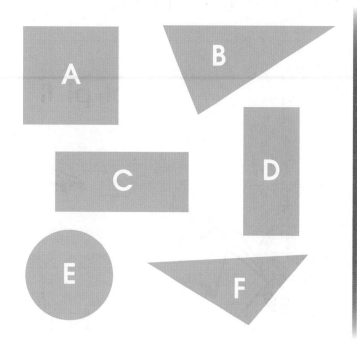

A _____

B _____

C _____

D _____

E _____

F _____

B. Look at Simon's picture. Help him count and write the number of each shape.

square: _____

triangle: _____

rectangle: _____

circle: _____

ISBN: 978-1-897457-96-2

C. Draw and name the shape you get when you trace each object on paper.

1.

Shape: _____

2.

Shape: ☐

3.

4.

Shape: ☐

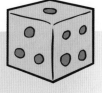

Shape: ☐

ISBN: 978-1-897457-96-2

Mathematics

D. Follow the instructions to complete the picture.

Steps to Draw Your Flower

- stalk: draw a long rectangle under the circle
- petals: draw 8 small circles around the circle
- leaves: draw a triangle on both sides of the rectangle

Draw a happy face on the big circle and colour your flower.

ISBN: 978-1-897457-96-2

E. **Compare the shapes. Circle the correct words or letters to complete the sentences.**

1.

A is **longer / shorter** .

A is **over / under** B.

2.

B is **bigger / smaller** .

B is **over / under** A.

3.

The circle is to the **left / right** of the square.

The circle is **bigger / smaller** than the square.

4.

A / B is taller.

A / B is wider.

ISBN: 978-1-897457-96-2

A. Name the shape that you see in each structure. Then draw a building with the four shapes. Colour your building.

circle   square   triangle   rectangle

1.

_____

2.

_____

3.

_____

4.

_____

My Building
(with the four shapes)

ISBN: 978-1-897457-96-2

B. Draw lines to show whether each structure is natural or human-made.

• **Natural** Structure

• **Human-made** Structure

Science Fun

The CN Tower in Toronto (553.33 m) is the tallest human-made free-standing structure in Canada.

ISBN: 978-1-897457-96-2 *Grade 1-2*

C. Structures often give shelter to us and other living things. Help the creatures find their way home through the maze.

The longest structure ever built by humans is the Great Wall of China. It is about 3500 km long.

ISBN: 978-1-897457-96-2

D. Some structures are built for other purposes than giving shelter. Do the matching to show the functions of the structures.

Some structures might have more than one function.

Functions of **Structures**

- to give protection

- to support a load

- to span a distance

ISBN: 978-1-897457-96-2

Social Studies

A. Write the numbers (1-7) to tell the order in which these daily events happen.

Daily Events

( ) I go to bed.

( ) I go to school.

( ) I eat breakfast.

( ) I do my homework.

( ) I eat lunch.

( ) I wake up.

( ) I have dinner.

B. Draw the hands on the clock faces to show the times at which you do these things.

Getting up

Leaving home for school

Going home from school

Going to bed

ISBN: 978-1-897457-96-2

C. Draw a picture for each special event. Write about each one.

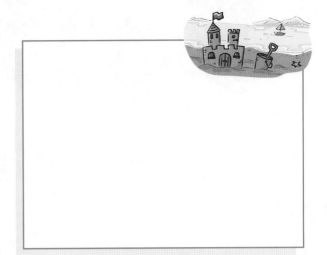

What you wish to have
for your birthday

_____

_____

_____

_____

What you did on your
last summer vacation

_____

_____

_____

_____

The best holiday
present you ever got

_____

_____

_____

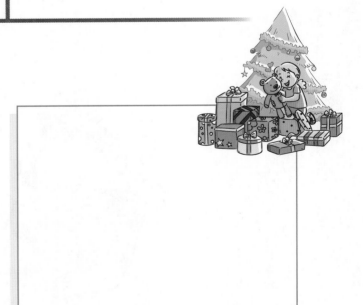

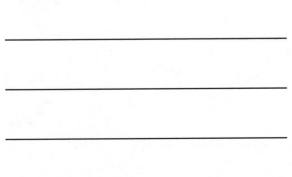

ISBN: 978-1-897457-96-2 *Grade 1-2*

Scribble Game

Try this game with a friend.

Materials:

- crayons or coloured pencils
- paper
- pencil

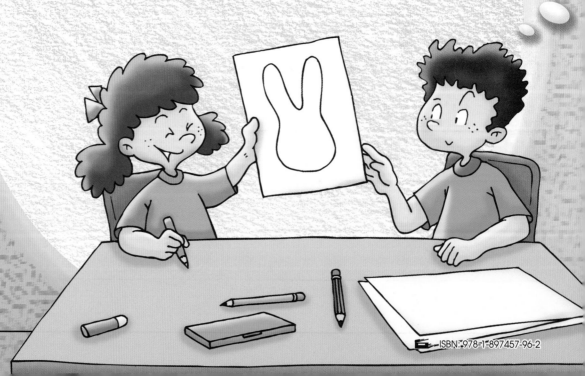

ISBN 978-1-897457-96-2

Directions:

1. Draw a closed figure.

2. Pass it to a friend.

3. Have him/her finish it.

Example 1

Example 2

ISBN: 978-1-897457-96-2

The Mouse-Deer's Trick

Part 2

...He was mean.

The mouse-deer and the flying squirrel went to see the tiger. They told him that the food was stolen by a fat, old tiger with a flying squirrel sitting on his nose.

The tiger was very angry.

Take me to him!

Sure! I'll lead you there.

82

ISBN: 978-1-897457-96-2

There he is!

The tiger was led to a wide river by the flying squirrel on his nose.

The tiger thought his reflection was the other tiger. He jumped into the water.

ROAR!

The tiger realized he was tricked. But it was too late.

Help...

Yummy!

Mission completed!

From then on, all animals could finally enjoy a snack by the salt lick.

The End

83

ISBN: 978-1-897457-96-2

Grade 1-2

The Water Park

What can be more enjoyable than getting wet and splashing in the water on a hot summer day?

The water park is the best place for you to beat the summer heat. With all the thrilling waterslides and wave pools, you will not have time to get bored. Many water parks provide life jackets for free, so even if you are not a good swimmer, you can still float around safely and simply relax in the fun-filled pool. You can also have fun on the interactive water play structures that are usually equipped with sprays, jets, hoses, water shooters, and tunnels to crawl in.

Why not soak up some summer fun with your family at the water park?

ISBN: 978-1-897457-96-2

WEEK 5

English

- read a story
- learn about camping items
- identify antonyms
- complete a word search

Mathematics

- name solids
- use position words
- classify shapes according to their attributes
- recognize patterns

Science

- relate objects to the materials from which they are made
- identify items that float and sink
- learn about energy

Social Studies

- identify special events in each month

Arts & Crafts

- weave a placemat

ISBN: 978-1-897457-96-2

A. Read the story. Then check ✔ the true sentences.

Camping *Fun*

Jason and his family are going camping this weekend. They will go to a lake up north. Jason likes to go there. They go there every year. There is just so much to do. He can swim with his parents, catch some fish, and explore the woods nearby. They will sleep in a big tent. It is a new tent that his dad bought for the trip. Their old one is broken.

1. Jason will play baseball with his dad and mom. ◯

2. Jason likes camping by the lake. ◯

3. Jason will sleep in the old tent. ◯

4. Jason can go fishing. ◯

5. Jason's father bought a new tent for the camping trip. ◯

6. Jason and his family go camping by the lake every year. ◯

ISBN: 978-1-897457-96-2

B. Check ✔ the things on the list that Jason needs for the trip. Then suggest one more thing he should take and answer the question.

1.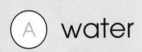

Packing List for Camping

(A) water

(B) vase   (C) sunscreen

(D) flashlight   (E) swimwear

(F) cap   (G) microwave

(H) compass   (I) garbage can

(J) piano   (K) insect repellent

(L) map   (✔) _____

2. Why must a tent be waterproof to be used for camping?

_____

_____

ISBN: 978-1-897457-96-2   *Grade 1-2*

C. Match each word with its opposite.

night	little	cold	in
sad	light	up	

Words that have opposite meanings are called antonyms.

big
small

1. big _____

2. down _____

3. heavy _____

4. day _____

5. out _____

6. happy _____

7. hot _____

8. Choose three pairs of opposite words from above. Use each pair in a sentence of your own.

*The squirrel is climbing **up** and **down** the tree.*

- _____

- _____

- _____

ISBN: 978-1-897457-96-2

D. Circle the following camping words in the word search.

tent   pillow   marshmallow   flashlight   fire
hot dog   campground   canoe   logs
mosquito   journal   matches

q	w	e	t	u	i	o	p	a	m	d	f	g
z	f	x	h	c	f	v	i	b	a	n	j	m
m	l	o	o	k	i	j	l	g	r	h	o	c
v	a	y	t	e	n	t	l	a	s	m	u	a
u	s	j	d	m	o	l	o	q	h	a	r	m
d	h	j	o	l	o	p	w	h	m	t	n	p
a	l	d	g	h	j	n	j	i	a	c	a	g
c	i	e	y	h	n	m	k	o	l	h	l	r
b	g	c	a	n	o	e	d	v	l	e	y	o
l	h	j	g	r	w	q	n	l	o	s	a	u
w	t	u	i	o	p	l	k	j	w	g	f	n
a	s	d	f	i	r	e	l	w	v	c	x	d
l	o	g	s		a	x	c	v	g	o	p	m
q	d	f	t	m	o	s	q	u	i	t	o

ISBN: 978-1-897457-96-2   *Grade 1-2*

A. Look at the solids. Write the names of the shapes in the boxes.

cylinder   sphere   cube   cone

1.

2.

3.

4.

B. Put the shapes in order.

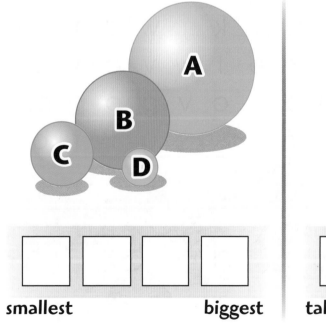

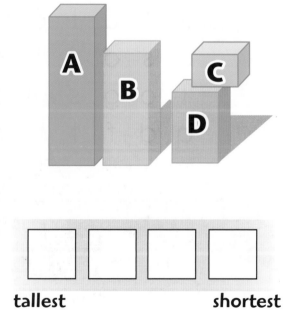

smallest   biggest   tallest   shortest

ISBN: 978-1-897457-96-2

Week 5

Mathematics

C. **Look at each group of shapes. Complete the sentences with the given words.**

in front of   between   on
under   over   behind
beside   inside

1. The cylinders are ＿＿＿＿＿＿ the cube.

   The cone is ＿＿＿＿＿＿ the cube.

   The sphere is ＿＿＿＿＿＿ the cylinders.

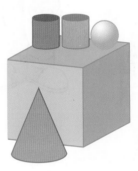

2. The sphere is ＿＿＿＿＿＿ the box.

   The cube is ＿＿＿＿＿＿ the box.

   The cube is ＿＿＿＿＿＿ the cylinder.

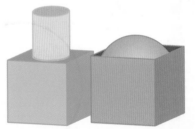

3. The cylinder is ＿＿＿＿＿＿ the sphere.

   The sphere is ＿＿＿＿＿＿ the cubes.

   The cone is ＿＿＿＿＿＿ the sphere.

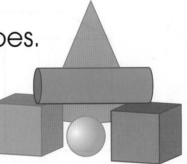

91

ISBN: 978-1-897457-96-2

D. Read what the children say and colour the shapes.

1.

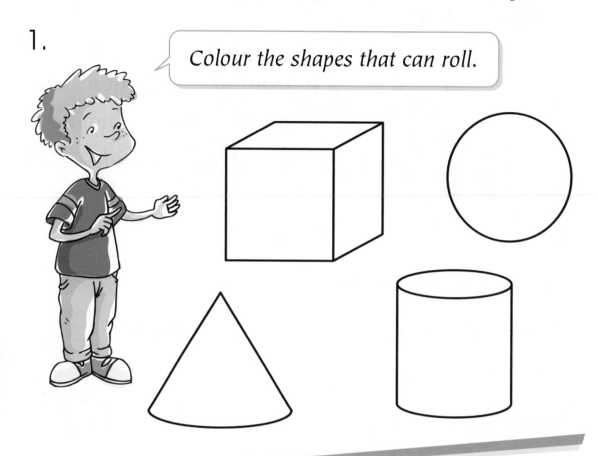

Colour the shapes that can roll.

2.

Colour the shapes that can be stacked up.

ISBN: 978-1-897457-96-2

E. Check ✔ the shapes that are cut into halves.

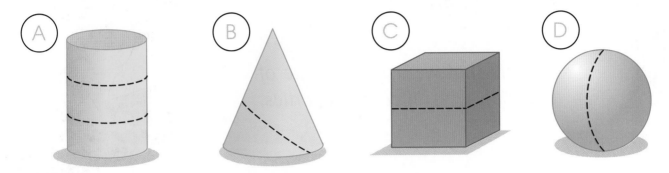

F. Follow the pattern and colour the shape that comes next in each group. Then circle the correct word to complete what the girl says.

1.

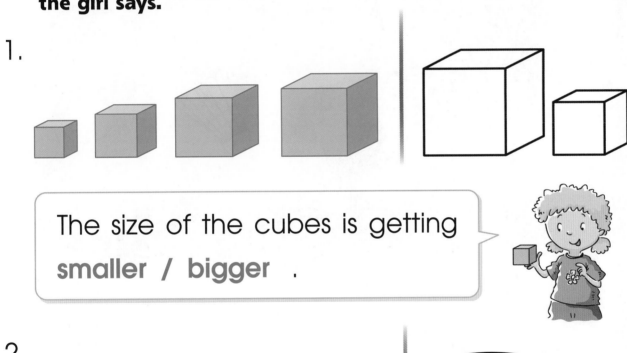

The size of the cubes is getting
smaller / bigger   .

2.

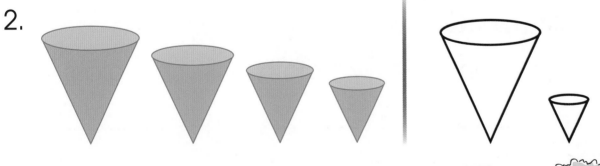

The height of the cones is getting
higher / lower   .

93

ISBN: 978-1-897457-96-2   *Grade 1-2*

A. Match each object with the material it is made of.

> *Objects that we use are made of materials with different properties.*

Objects

Materials

iron	cloth	glass
_____	_____	_____

feather	wood
_____	_____

ISBN: 978-1-897457-96-2

B. **Write "F" for the things that float and "S" for the things that sink.**

Float *or* Sink

C. **Do the activity to find out what things float and what things do not.**

Instructions:

- Fill up a bucket or a sink with water.

- Choose 3 objects to put in the water.

- Guess whether each object will float or sink.

- Put the objects in the water and record the results.

Object	My Guess	My Observations

95

ISBN: 978-1-897457-96-2

D. Decide whether or not each thing needs energy. Then give another example for each category.

Things that **Need Energy**	Things that **Do Not Need Energy**
Example:	Example:
_____	_____

ISBN: 978-1-897457-96-2

E. **The children show you how energy is used. Fill in the blanks to complete what they say.**

grow   change   think   move

1.

It takes energy to _____ .

It takes energy to _____ .

2.

It takes energy to _____ .

It takes energy to _____ .

ISBN: 978-1-897457-96-2

Match the special events with the months of the year.

Civic Holiday   Easter Monday   Valentine's Day

Mother's Day   Remembrance Day   Canada Day

Boxing Day   Thanksgiving Day

January

_____

February

_____

May

_____

June

_____

September

_____

October

_____

ISBN: 978-1-897457-96-2

Good Friday   Labour Day

Father's Day   Christmas Day

New Year's Day

There are two events that are in either March or April.

March

_____

April

_____

July

_____

August

_____

November

_____

December

_____

99

Placemat Weaving

Materials:

- **2 sheets of coloured paper**
- **scissors**
- **pencil**

Directions:

1

Fold paper in half.

2

Draw lines from fold to 2 cm from edge.

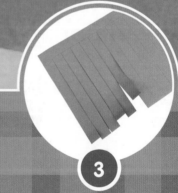

3

Cut on the lines.

ISBN: 978-1-897457-96-2

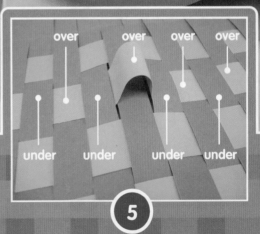

Take strips and "weave" over and under.

4

Cut the other sheet of paper into strips 2.5 cm wide.

over · over · over · over

under · under · under · under

5

Weave over and under as shown.

ISBN: 978-1-897457-96-2

COMICS

Sam's Birthday Surprise

It was Sam's birthday. His parents gave him an alien spaceship as a gift. Sam loved it. He loved aliens.

Thank you, Mommy and Daddy!

Sam got on the school bus. His friends wished him "happy birthday".

We have a surprise for you. But you'll have to wait.

During lunchtime, Sam's friends were busy preparing a party for Sam.

Do you think we have enough table tennis balls?

ISBN: 978-1-897457-96-2

They cut holes in some boxes. Then they painted the boxes.

Sam did not notice this. He was busy playing with his spaceship.

Suddenly, Sam returned to the classroom. His friends quickly hid everything.

Weee...beep beep!

After school, Sam realized that the school bus was emptier than usual. But he did not think too much about it. He continued to play with his new spaceship.

To be continued...

ISBN: 978-1-897457-96-2

Grade 1-2

Centre Island

A short ferry ride from downtown Toronto, Ontario takes you to Centre Island, where you can have lots of summer fun in the sun.

On Centre Island, you can swim at a sandy beach, run through a hedge maze, or simply bike, rollerblade, or stroll around the island. When you are tired and hungry, you can have a picnic under the shade of trees with your family. If you fancy something more exciting, there is an amusement park for kids of your age with fun rides, like a carousel, a Ferris wheel, a rocking ferry, and a swan ride.

Hop on a ferry, get away from the city, and have another day filled with laughter this summer!

ISBN: 978-1-897457-96-2

WEEK 6

English

- read a story
- identify sentences that do not belong in paragraphs
- learn synonyms
- learn palindromes

Mathematics

- solve probability problems
- do addition and subtraction
- follow number patterns
- identify shapes

Science

- identify solids and liquids
- identify water around you
- learn that water melts and freezes

Social Studies

- identify places in a community
- identify community workers

Arts & Crafts

- make a butterfly with coffee filters

ISBN: 978-1-897457-96-2

Week 6

A. Read the story. Then check ✔ the true sentences.

Pancake Breakfast

Thank you, Grandma.

Rob sat at the table waiting for his favourite breakfast food. Pancakes! His grandma came to visit and she is very good at making pancakes. Grandma gave Rob a big pancake. Rob smeared butter and poured sweet maple syrup on it. He took a huge bite and it was just delicious. Grandma promised to teach him how to make pancakes. Soon, Rob would be able to make pancake breakfast for his family.

1. Rob's grandma lives with Rob.

2. Rob wants to buy pancake breakfast for his family.

3. Rob likes pancakes for breakfast.

4. Rob's grandma makes yummy pancakes.

5. Grandma will teach Rob how to make pancakes.

ISBN: 978-1-897457-96-2

B. Read each paragraph. One sentence does not belong. Cross out this sentence.

1.
Jane's family was spending the day at the beach. Jane and her sister Jessica decided to build a sandcastle. First they filled their bucket with sand. The red wagon was in the garage. Then Jessica added some water to it.

2. Each night a skunk would come into Ann's backyard. The skunk had shiny black fur and a fluffy tail. The feathers were very soft. It had a big white stripe running down the middle of its back. Ann knew if she stayed away from the skunk, it would stay away from her.

3.
Sharon likes cycling. She has a red bike. It was a birthday present from her father last year. Her father works at a bank. Sometimes, Sharon goes biking with her friends. They are careful. They always wear helmets.

ISBN: 978-1-897457-96-2 *Grade 1-2*

C. **Draw a line to match each word with its synonym. Then rewrite each sentence using the synonym of the underlined word.**

1.

> *Synonyms are words with similar meanings.*

start •   • difficult

hard •   • unhappy

weeping •   • crying

sad •   • begin

quick •   • fast

2. The baby was <u>weeping</u>.

_____

3. It was <u>hard</u> to pedal my bicycle up the hill.

_____

4. We will <u>begin</u> the game now!

_____

5. Sharon is <u>unhappy</u> to see her friend leave.

_____

6. That is a <u>quick</u> skunk!

_____

ISBN: 978-1-897457-96-2

D. Use the code to write each palindrome.

> *Palindromes are words that read the same forwards and backwards.*

Code

1. a young dog:

   $\overline{}$ $\overline{}$ $\overline{}$
   16 21 16

2. a part of the face:

   $\overline{}$ $\overline{}$ $\overline{}$
   5   25   5

3. something a baby needs:

   $\overline{}$ $\overline{}$ $\overline{}$
   2   9   2

4. the middle of the day:

   $\overline{}$ $\overline{}$ $\overline{}$ $\overline{}$
   14 15 15 14

5. another name for father:

   $\overline{}$ $\overline{}$ $\overline{}$
   4   1   4

6. another name for mother:

   $\overline{}$ $\overline{}$ $\overline{}$
   13 15 13

ISBN: 978-1-897457-96-2

A. Circle or draw the correct answers.

1. David will **always / sometimes / never** pick a  .

2. Is there a better chance that David will pick

   a. a ⭐ or a 🤍 ?

   b. a 🤍 or a 🔴 ?

3.  Lucy will **always / sometimes / never** pick a ⭐ or 🔴 .

4. Is there a better chance that Lucy will pick a ⭐ or a 🔴 ?

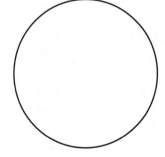

ISBN: 978-1-897457-96-2

B. Solve the problems.

1. There are 6  and 7 ⚪ .

How many marbles are there in all?

_____ marbles

$+$ _____

2. There are 4 small  and 8 big .

How many dolls are there in all?

_____ dolls

3. There are 16  in the box. Sue takes out 9.

How many puppets are left in the box?

_____ puppets

4. There are 15 cars in the box. 7  are green.

How many cars are not green?

_____ cars

ISBN: 978-1-897457-96-2

C. Write the numbers in the boxes to show the number of each kind of animal in the zoo.

3 ones

5 tens

4 tens 2 ones

7 tens 9 ones

D. Fill in the missing numbers.

1.

42 44   48   54   58

2.

35 40   55   65

ISBN: 978-1-897457-96-2

Mathematics

E. **The shapes are made with different coloured wires. Name and count the shapes.**

1.

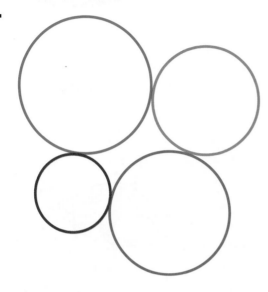

Shape:

_____ ; ☐

2.

Shape:

_____ ; ☐

3.

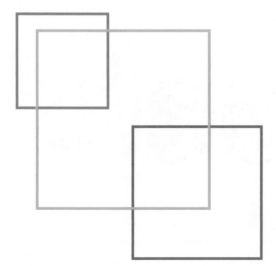

Shape:

_____ ; ☐

4.

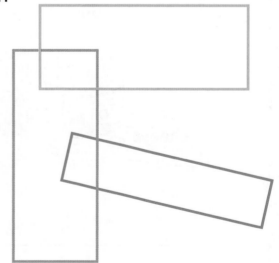

Shape:

_____ ; ☐

ISBN: 978-1-897457-96-2

A. Match the tool with the thing(s) that the tool can hold.

Tool

Thing

 paper
towel

 glass
bowl

 basket •

• water

• salt

• strawberry

B. List the solid items in the mixing bowl and the liquid items in the measuring cup.

cheese   Oil   Sugar   Milk   Juice   Flour

_____

_____

_____

_____

_____

_____

ISBN: 978-1-897457-96-2

C. Solid or liquid? Solve each riddle and check ✔ the items that belong.

> *Liquids flow and take the shape of their container. Solids don't change their shape easily.*

1. My shape is constant,

   I don't take another.

   Whether I'm in a bowl,

   Or the purse of your mother.

 **What am I?**

   _____

2. I take on the shape

   Of whatever I'm in.

   A pan or a vase

   Or a box or a tin.

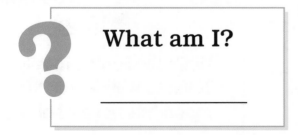 **What am I?**

   _____

ISBN: 978-1-897457-96-2 *Grade 1-2*

D. Water is a liquid and is all around us. Colour the water blue.

Science Fun

While the Earth is mostly covered with water, the moon has none at all!

ISBN: 978-1-897457-96-2

E. Determine whether the water is "solid" or "liquid" in each picture. Then fill in the blanks.

melts   freezes   water   ice

1.

_____   _____

The water _____ and becomes _____ .

2.

_____   _____

The ice _____ and becomes _____ .

ISBN: 978-1-897457-96-2

A. A community is a place where people live, play, and work. Match the pictures of the places with their names.

zoo   library   school   hospital   fire hall   park

1. _____

2. _____

Community

3. _____

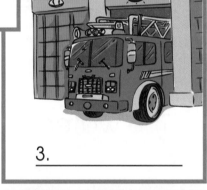

4. _____

5. _____

6. _____

ISBN: 978-1-897457-96-2

B. **Match the tools with the community workers. Then name the community worker each child describes.**

1. teacher

2. firefighter

3. mail carrier

4. nurse

A

B

C

D

5. *He takes my temperature.* _____

6. *He brings me letters.* _____

7. *She teaches me math.* _____

 ISBN: 978-1-897457-96-2

Butterfly Arts

Materials:

- coffee filters
- pipe cleaners
- markers
- glue
- spray bottle filled with water

1.

2.

3.

Don't forget the antennae!

ISBN: 978-1-897457-96-2

5.

4.

Directions:

1. Lay coffee filter flat on table.

2. Colour filter with markers.

3. Hold up filter and spray with water.

4. Lay out to dry.

5. Repeat the same with another filter.

6. Use 2 pipe cleaners to form the shape of antennae. Twist another pipe cleaner around to join them.

7. Glue the two filters and pipe cleaners as shown.

ISBN: 978-1-897457-96-2

COMICS

Sam's Birthday Surprise

Part 2

See you soon, Mom!

I'm sure Sam will love the alien cake.

Around five o'clock, Sam's dad told Sam, "I'm taking you out to your friends' surprise." Sam was excited.

Meanwhile, Sam's friends were finishing the preparations.

Sam was surprised that his dad dropped him off at school.

ISBN: 978-1-897457-96-2

Sam opened the door...

Surprise!

They all looked like aliens. It was an alien birthday party.

Make a wish!

And blow the candles!

Sam put on an alien outfit too. They played party games and ate the alien cake. Sam's birthday party was a perfect surprise!

The End

ISBN: 978-1-897457-96-2

Grade 1-2

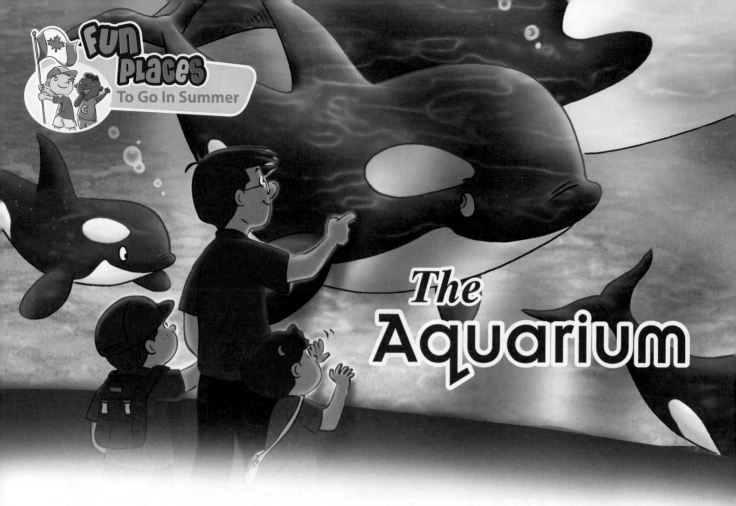

The Aquarium

The aquarium is a great summer attraction.

Many aquaria welcome you with a shallow touch pool where you can touch small sea animals, like starfish and hermit crabs. Then you will step into an underwater world without getting wet. The tanks are so big that you will feel like you're walking in a deep ocean, with thousands of bright-coloured fish, and even sharks, swimming around you. You can watch divers feed them by hand too! You will see animal stars, such as dolphins, seals, and killer whales, performing their stunning skills in shows. You may even get a chance to feed the seals and touch the dolphins!

Visiting the aquarium is a great way to cool off on a hot summer day.

ISBN: 978-1-897457-96-2

WEEK 7

English
- read a story and correct sentences
- use capital letters with proper nouns
- learn some new words
- write a postcard

Mathematics
- compare capacities of containers
- solve problems about capacity
- identify shapes

Science
- learn about different cycles
- learn the Earth's daily cycle
- explore temperature change
- relate shadows to times of the day

Social Studies
- learn about some rules
- identify good and bad behaviours

Arts & Crafts
- make a caterpillar

ISBN: 978-1-897457-96-2

Week 7

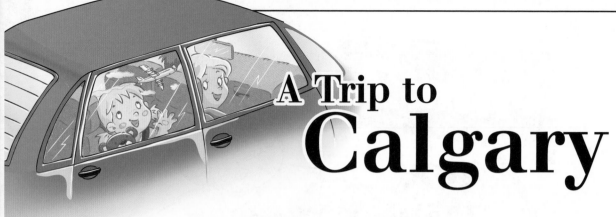

A Trip to Calgary

A. Read the story. Then put a line through the wrong word in each sentence and write the correct word above it.

Sabrina had her face pressed to the window of the family car. She was staring at a large airplane as it was taking off. Soon Sabrina would be flying through the sky. She was going to Calgary to visit her cousin Josie.

It was time to board the plane. Sabrina hugged her father and mother and said goodbye. A flight attendant helped Sabrina find her seat. As she looked out of the window, Sabrina saw that the plane was leaving the ground. She was flying! Soon she would be in Calgary with Josie.

1. Sabrina was staring at a small plane.

2. Sabrina would be jumping through the sky.

3. A flight attendant helped Sabrina find her backpack.

4. The plane was leaving the sky.

ISBN: 978-1-897457-96-2

B. Give short answers to the questions.

1. How did Sabrina get to the airport?

   _____

2. Where was she going?

   _____

3. | *Who am I going to visit?* |

   _____

4. | *Who helped me find my seat?* |

   _____

C. Rewrite each sentence using capital letters for the proper nouns.

1. sabrina left toronto on an airplane.

   _____

2. She landed in calgary, alberta at 11:00 a.m.

   _____

3. Her cousin josie met her at the airport.

   _____

4. I flew to halifax with my friend peter.

   _____

ISBN: 978-1-897457-96-2

D. Read the clues and complete the crossword puzzle with words from the story.

Across

A. your aunt's son or daughter
B. It travels in the sky.
C. moving in the air
D. get on
E. We stand on it.

Down

1. looking
2. He or she helps you on the plane.
3. where you sit

ISBN: 978-1-897457-96-2

E. **Read the postcard that Sabrina sent to her parents. Then write a postcard to a friend about a place you visited and what you did there.**

Dear Mom and Dad,

I'm having a great time in Calgary. Yesterday, Josie and I went horseback riding. My horse's name was Smokey. Today we will go shopping. See you soon.

Love,
Sabrina

To:

Mr. and Mrs. Lake
99 Church Street,
Toronto, Ontario
L4S 4M2

To:

_____

_____

_____

_____

_____

_____

_____

_____

ISBN: 978-1-897457-96-2

A. Colour the containers.

more than 1 cup: red
less than 1 cup: blue

B. Choose the best object to measure the capacity of each of the containers. Write the letters.

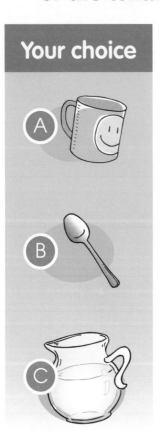

Your choice

A

B

C

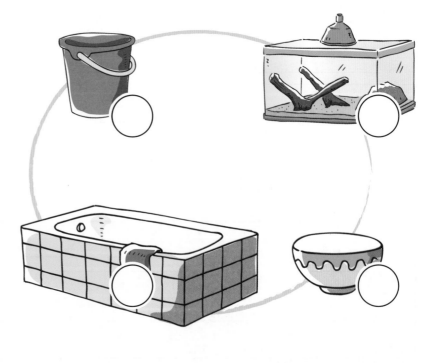

ISBN: 978-1-897457-96-2

C. **See how many cups of water each container can hold. Solve the problems.**

1. How many cups of water can

    a. a pot hold? _____ cups

    b. a bottle hold? _____ cups

2. Which container has

    a. the greatest capacity? _____

    b. the least capacity? _____

3. How many pots of water are needed to fill a pail?

    _____ pots

4. If the jug is half-filled with water, how many more cups of water are needed to fill up the jug?

    _____ more

ISBN: 978-1-897457-96-2

D. Look at the graph. Then answer the questions.

Number of Glasses of Water the Containers Hold

jug — 🥛 🥛 🥛

kettle — 🥛 🥛 🥛 🥛 🥛

tank — 🥛 🥛 🥛 🥛 🥛 🥛 🥛

mug — 🥛 🥛

bottle — 🥛 🥛 🥛

1. Which container, a bottle or a mug, has a greater capacity?

   _____

2. How many glasses of water can

   a. a kettle hold? _____ glasses

   b. a tank and a kettle hold? _____ glasses

3. Which of the containers above is best for measuring the capacity of a bathtub?

   _____

ISBN: 978-1-897457-96-2

Mathematics

E. Colour the container that can be traced to get each shape.

ISBN: 978-1-897457-96-2

A. **Some changes in our daily lives occur in cycles. Fill in the blanks to complete the different cycles.**

evening   afternoon   dinner   lunch   night

Daily Meals

breakfast

Times of the Day

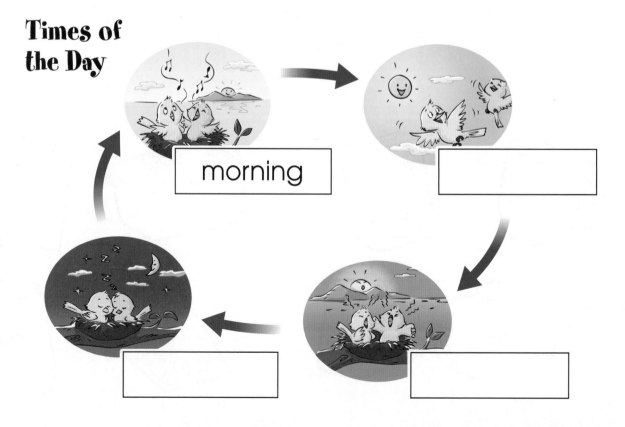

morning

ISBN: 978-1-897457-96-2

B. Circle the correct words. Colour the part of the Earth where it is daytime yellow and the part where it is nighttime blue.

The sun gives us   light / air   and heat. The Earth   spins / jumps   to give us day and night.   It is   daytime / nighttime   on the part of the Earth that faces the sun and   daytime / nighttime   on the part not facing the sun. It takes about 24   hours / seconds   for the Earth to complete a daily   cycle / meal   .

Science Fun

When we are getting into bed for a nice long sleep, someone on the other side of the Earth is getting up!

ISBN: 978-1-897457-96-2

C. **Draw lines to match the thermometers with the pictures.**

One day is the time taken for the Earth to complete one turn. The temperature changes as the Earth turns.

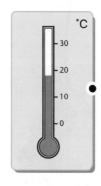

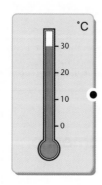

ISBN: 978-1-897457-96-2

D. Colour the correct pictures to show the shadows and times of the day.

Shadows and Times of the Day

shadow

8 o'clock morning

12 o'clock noon

2 o'clock afternoon

5 o'clock afternoon

ISBN: 978-1-897457-96-2

A. Look at the rules. Check ✔ the pictures that show children following the rules. Then write one rule in your family.

> *There are rules for everyone. Some rules keep us safe; some help us get along with one another at home, at school, and in our community.*

Rules

- No littering.

- No loud music after 8:00 p.m.

- Keep things tidy.

- Wear a helmet when riding a bicycle.

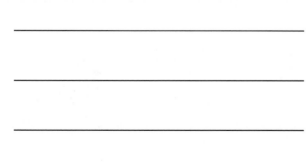

A Rule in My Family

_____

_____

_____

_____

ISBN: 978-1-897457-96-2

B. There are rules for behaviour at school. Draw to tell whether the children show good or bad behaviour.

 good behaviour   bad behaviour

ISBN: 978-1-897457-96-2

Egg-Carton Caterpillar

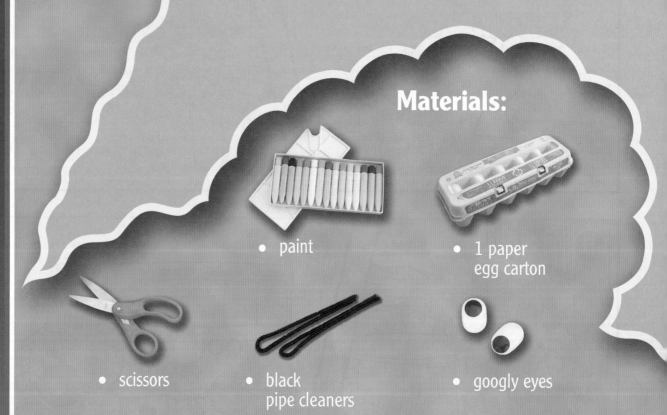

Materials:

- paint

- 1 paper egg carton

- scissors

- black pipe cleaners

- googly eyes

ISBN: 978-1-897457-96-2

Directions:

1. Cut off egg carton cover.

2. Cut egg carton in half.

3. Paint carton green. Let dry.

4. Tie the two rows together with a pipe cleaner.

5. Add pipe cleaner legs.

6. Add googly eyes.

Give your caterpillar a cute name.

ISBN: 978-1-897457-96-2

The Puppet Show

One day, a family found a box in the attic. It was covered with dust. They opened the box and found puppets inside.

The next day, the children showed their class the puppets.

The class decided to make new clothes for the puppets.

ISBN: 978-1-897457-96-2

They also made a puppet theatre. It had a woodland scene.

They learned to make the puppets move and walk.

Then they wrote a story about the puppets.

Let's put on a puppet show.

Yeah!

The teacher said to the class, "Why don't we put on a puppet show for the whole school?" The children agreed and were very excited.

To be continued...

ISBN: 978-1-897457-96-2

Grade 1-2

Nature Reserves

Summer is the season when plants flourish and animals are active. It is also a great time for you to get close to nature.

A nature reserve is where rare and endangered wildlife species are protected in their natural habitats, like forests and wetlands. You can take a walk along trails and see some endangered plants, like the butternut tree and the American chestnut. You may even be lucky enough to see an animal at risk, such as the golden eagle or the eastern mole. There is usually a centre in a nature reserve where you can learn more about the different species living there.

When you are in a nature reserve, remember to stay on marked trails. Never feed any animals or remove any plants or rocks. Respect nature and have fun!

ISBN: 978-1-897457-96-2

WEEK 8

English

- read a recipe
- write short answers
- read and draw
- compare and contrast two things

Mathematics

- count coins
- write times
- do counting
- draw and name shapes

Science

- learn the yearly seasonal cycle
- identify suitable seasonal clothing
- explore changes in living things in different seasons

Social Studies

- identify things to be put in the recycling box
- learn to reuse things

Arts & Crafts

- make binoculars

Week 8

ISBN: 978-1-897457-96-2

A. Read the recipe for making sugar cookies.

Ingredients:

- $\frac{3}{4}$ cup of softened butter
- 1 cup of white sugar
- 2 eggs
- $\frac{1}{2}$ teaspoon of vanilla extract
- $2\frac{1}{2}$ cups of flour
- 3 teaspoons of milk
- 1 teaspoon of baking powder
- $\frac{1}{2}$ teaspoon of salt

Directions:

1. In a large bowl, mix together the butter, milk, and sugar until it is smooth. Beat in the eggs and the vanilla extract.

2. Stir in the flour, baking powder, and salt.

3. Cover and chill the dough in the refrigerator for one hour.

4. Roll out the dough on a floured surface. Cut into shapes with any cookie cutters. Place cookies on an ungreased cookie sheet.

5. Bake 6 to 8 minutes in the heated oven. Cool completely.

English

ISBN: 978-1-897457-96-2

B. Check ✔ the ingredients for making sugar cookies.

○ salt ○ pepper

○ flour ○ vanilla extract

○ sugar ○ chocolate chips

C. Give short answers to the following questions.

1. Which three things do you mix together first?

_____

2. How long does it take to chill the dough?

_____

3. What can you use to cut the dough into shapes?

_____

4. Where should you place the cookies to bake them?

_____

5. How long does it take to bake the cookies?

_____

ISBN: 978-1-897457-96-2

D. Read, draw, and colour.

1. Draw some cookies on the plate.
2. Draw some apples in the tree.
3. Add a star on the back of the chair.
4. Draw a flower in the picture frame.
5. Colour the picture.

ISBN: 978-1-897457-96-2

E. Match the animals with what they say about themselves. Then complete the sentences.

1.

- • "I can be a pet."
- • "I have fur."
- • "I bark."
- • "I have a tail."
- • "I chase mice."
- • "I purr."

When we compare two things, we think about how they are the same. When we contrast two things, we think about how they are different.

2. Dogs and cats are the same because

_____

_____

3. Dogs and cats are different because

_____

_____

ISBN: 978-1-897457-96-2

A. Write the cost of each item. Then check ✔ the correct number of coins to answer each question.

1. ☐ ¢

2. ☐ ¢

3. ☐ ¢

4. ☐ ¢

5. Sue pays  for a . What is her change?

6. Ben buys 1 and 1 . How much does he pay?

ISBN: 978-1-897457-96-2

B. Write the times. Then put the events in order.

Events in Order (1-4)

o'clock

half past

ISBN: 978-1-897457-96-2

C. Count and write the numbers to complete the sentences.

1. There are _____ ducks on the log.

2. _____ duck is standing on a rock.

3. _____ ducks are swimming.

4. There are _____ ducks in all.

5. There is a total of _____ flowers.

6. _____ of the flowers are yellow.

7. There are _____ butterflies.

8. There are _____ clouds in the sky.

ISBN: 978-1-897457-96-2

D. **Trace the dotted lines to draw each shape. Then redraw the shape next to it and name the shape.**

This is a 1. _____

2. _____

3. _____

ISBN: 978-1-897457-96-2

A. Name the season shown in each picture. Then colour the suitable clothing for the season.

spring   summer   fall   winter

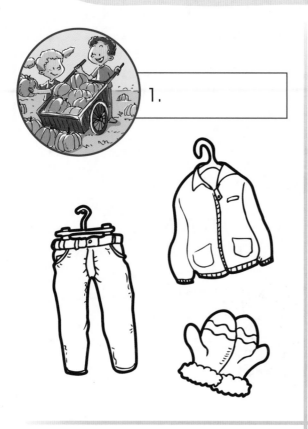

1.

2.

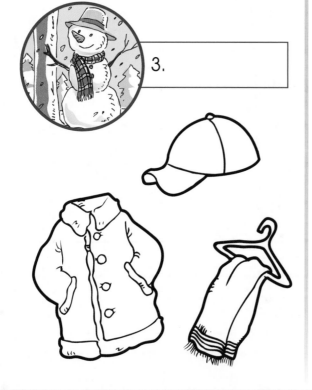

3.

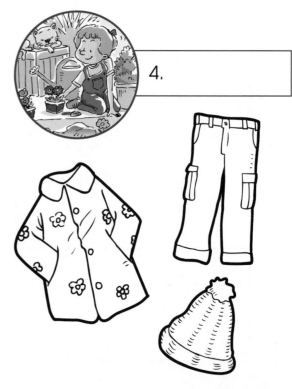

4.

ISBN: 978-1-897457-96-2

B. Put the seasons in order, starting with spring. Check ✔ what happens in each season. Then name your favourite season and write three sentences about it.

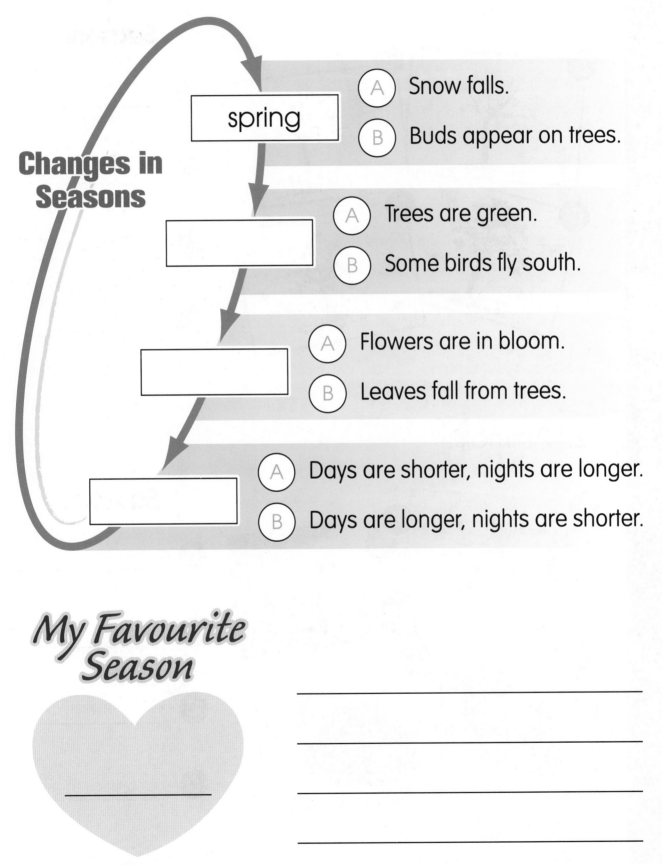

Changes in Seasons

spring

A) Snow falls.

B) Buds appear on trees.

A) Trees are green.

B) Some birds fly south.

A) Flowers are in bloom.

B) Leaves fall from trees.

A) Days are shorter, nights are longer.

B) Days are longer, nights are shorter.

My Favourite Season

_____

_____

_____

_____

ISBN: 978-1-897457-96-2

C. Plants and animals change with the seasons. Write the name of the season shown in each picture.

1. Plants

Seasons

A _____

B _____

C _____

D _____

2. Animals

Seasons

A _____

B _____

C _____

D _____

ISBN: 978-1-897457-96-2

D. Fill in the blanks. Then trace the arrows and name the seasons.

| summer | seasonal | sun | year |

The Earth goes around the <u>1._____</u> . It takes the Earth about one <u>2._____</u> to go around the sun once. It is this trip that gives us in Canada the yearly <u>3._____</u> cycle with the four seasons: spring, <u>4._____</u> , fall, and winter.

The Seasonal Cycle

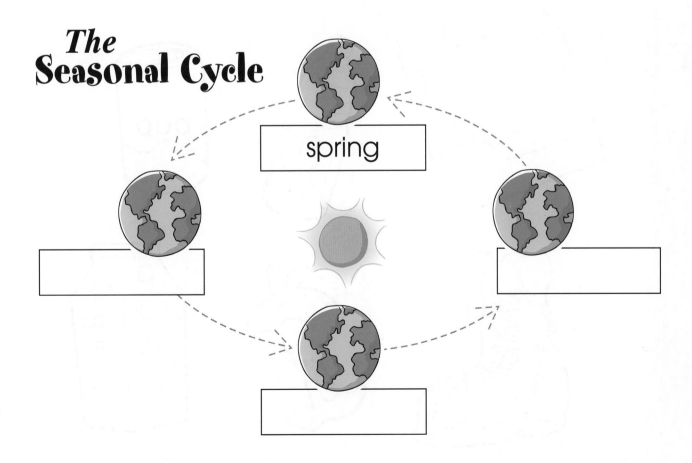

spring

ISBN: 978-1-897457-96-2

A. Colour the things that can go into the recycling box.

> *There are many ways to show that we care about our environment. One way is to reduce, reuse, and recycle things.*

ISBN: 978-1-897457-96-2

B. Check ✔ the possible ways to reuse yogourt cups. Then fill in the blanks to see how to make a maraca with two yogourt cups.

Ways To Reuse Yogourt Cups:

(A) holders for paper clips

(B) buckets for small sandcastles

(C) wrappers for gifts

(D) holders for sandwiches

(E) small plant pots

Making a Maraca with Yogourt Cups

Steps:

tape   clean   rice

1. _____ the yogourt cups.

2. Fill one cup with _____ .

3. Secure the cups with _____ .

159

ISBN: 978-1-897457-96-2

Arts & Crafts

Materials:

- 2 toilet paper rolls
- single hole punch
- glue
- paint
- string

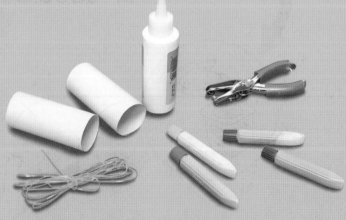

ISBN: 978-1-897457-96-2

Binoculars

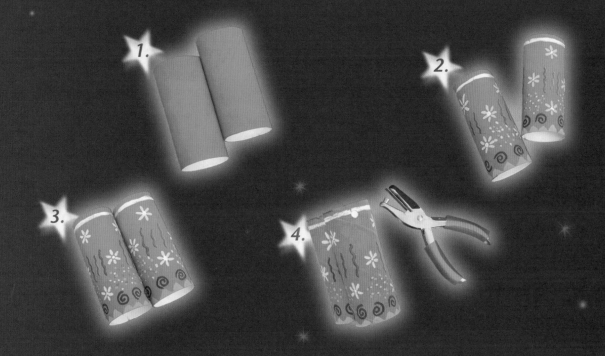

Directions:

1. Paint and draw some patterns on paper rolls. Let dry.

2. Glue rolls together on sides.

3. Punch holes in sides of rolls.

4. Tie string through the holes. Done.

ISBN: 978-1-897457-96-2

The Puppet Show

The class performed their puppet show. They spoke the puppets' lines and made them dance. The whole school enjoyed it!

This is amazing!

Have a great summer!

Then the school was closed for the summer holidays.

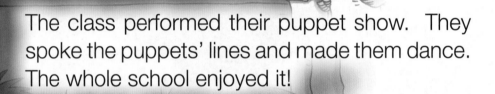

SCHOOL CLOSED FOR SUMMER HOLIDAYS

The children put the puppets back and ran home.

ISBN: 978-1-897457-96-2

Hurry up, guys!

That night, one puppet pushed open the lid of the box.

The puppets ran out of the town and into the woods.

All the puppets are gone!

Who took them?

The puppets danced and sang, "We can move on our own!"

The summer holidays were over. The children returned to school. They were surprised to find the box empty. They could never imagine that the puppets could make their own puppet show.

The End

ISBN: 978-1-897457-96-2

Grade 1-2

Toronto's Waterfront

Taking a leisurely walk along the boardwalk, playing volleyball on the beach, and enjoying the beautiful view of Lake Ontario – are these the only things you can do at Toronto's waterfront? Of course not! You can also have great fun at Harbourfront Centre, which is Canada's leading centre for the arts and culture of our time.

A series of festivals are held there each weekend during the summer. You can learn different dance forms, make your own musical instrument and play music with it, create your own hand puppet and put on a puppet show on the outdoor stage, and even learn to be a ringmaster or a circus performer.

Get outside and heat up your summer fun with singing, dancing, games, and more!

164

ISBN: 978-1-897457-96-2

ISBN: 978-1-897457-96-2

Swimming

Circle the correct words.

Do...

✓ wear swimming goggles / glasses

✓ swim when there is a lifeguard or an animal / adult around

✓ do warm-up exercises before / after swimming

✓ leave the water at the first sign of lightning / wind

✓ call for help when there is an emergency / ant

166

ISBN: 978-1-897457-96-2

Don't run, Sam!

Don't...

- ❌ walk / run around the pool

- ❌ swim when you do not feel well / sick

- ❌ swim right after thinking / eating

- ❌ swim when there is a / no "no swimming" sign

- ❌ pretend to be drowning or cry for help / wink in jest

ISBN: 978-1-897457-96-2

Biking

Circle the correct words. Then match each rule with the correct person or object.

Rule 1 Wear a helmet and fasten the straps securely under your nose / chin .

Rule 2 Wear sneakers / slippers or running shoes.

Rule 3 Always bike with an adult / umbrella .

Rule 4 Bike in a park or on car / bike lanes.

Rule 5 Always keep both hands on the handlebars / wheels .

ISBN: 978-1-897457-96-2

ISBN: 978-1-897457-96-2

Rollerblading

Read the rules and cut and paste the correct pictures.

Rule 1 Always wear a helmet, wrist guards, elbow pads, and knee pads.

Rule 2 Control your speed; never skate too fast.

Rule 3 Never push or pull fellow skaters.

Rule 4 Skate with an adult.

Rule 5 Practise basic skating skills on a flat, smooth surface.

ISBN: 978-1-897457-96-2

ISBN: 978-1-897457-96-2

ISBN: 978-1-897457-96-2

Picnic Time

Match the rules with the correct pictures. Write the numbers.

1 Wash your hands before eating.

2 Apply insect repellent.

3 Keep the lids of coolers closed after use.

4 Stay away from barbecue grills.

5 Cover all cooked food.

ISBN: 978-1-897457-96-2

Grade 1–2

ISBN: 978-1-897457-96-2

At a Playground

Put a cross ✗ on the children who show wrong playground behaviour.

Rules to Follow

1. Don't skip rungs on a stair.

2. Don't play ball games on playground equipment.

3. Never lean out or climb over the handrail.

4. Don't slide the wrong way.

5. Don't walk up the slide.

6. Don't stay near the bottom of the fire pole.

7. Don't stand on a swing.

8. Never walk close to the swing when someone is playing.

ISBN: 978-1-897457-96-2

ISBN: 978-1-897457-96-2

Answers
Grade 1-2

ISBN: 978-1-897457-96-2

Week 1

English

A. 1. fun   2. flew
   3. days   4. school
   5. friends   6. till
   7. end   8. We

B. 1. baseball   2. biking
   3. boating   4. camping
   5. fishing   6. hiking
   7. rollerblading   8. soccer
   9. swimming   10. tennis

C.

b	u	s	s	o	c	c	e	r	g	s	r
i	e	t	w	j	l	r	c	l	e	m	o
k	h	f	i	s	h	i	n	g	p	q	l
i	g	j	m	b	a	s	e	b	a	l	l
n	i	o	m	v	i	p	a	l	r	s	e
g	a	i	i	e	j	o	s	c	h	s	r
t	e	n	n	i	s	u	d	a	z	d	b
p	k	v	g	l	e	y	f	m	x	f	l
r	h	s	e	p	q	t	g	p	c	g	a
t	f	t	u	t	a	r	j	i	v	y	d
h	i	k	i	n	g	e	k	n	b	k	i
y	w	k	s	o	c	w	l	g	n	o	n
c	d	b	o	a	t	i	n	g	m	v	g

D. (Individual writing and drawing)

Mathematics

A. 1.

2.
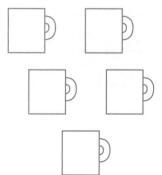

3.
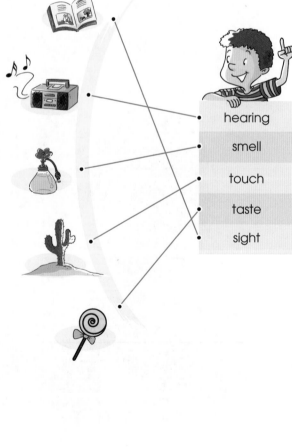

B. 1. behind   2. in front of
   3. behind   4. on
   5. above   6. under

C. (Individual colouring)
   1. nine   2. Two
   3. Six   4. Five
   5. six   6. one
   7. Two

D. 1. crayon: 6 ; paintbrush: 2 ; paint: 4
   2. 4   3. 3

Science

A.
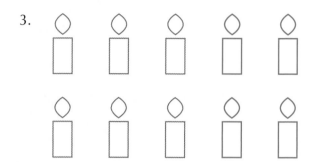

hearing

smell

touch

taste

sight

ISBN: 978-1-897457-96-2

B. 1. taste   2. sight
   3. smell   4. touch
   5. hearing

C. 1. plant   2. animal
   3. animal   4. animal
   5. plant

D. 1. non-living   2. living
   3. living   4. non-living
   5. non-living   6. living
   7. living

Social Studies

(Individual answers)

Week 2

English

A. 1. at 9:00 a.m.
   2. at 3:00 p.m.
   3. on Saturday and Sunday
   4. toys, clothes, furniture, and comic books

B. Furniture:
   chair ; desk ; couch ; table ; bed
   Toy:
   doll ; teddy bear ; baseball ; skipping rope ; jigsaw puzzle
   Clothing:
   pants ; coat ; dress ; hat ; scarf

C. 1. . ; .   2. ? ; !
   3. !

D. duck ; pan ; cup ; book ; lamp ; pig
   kite ; sun ; hair ; bike

Mathematics

A. 1. 1 ; 3 ; 7 ; 3   2. 14
   3. 3
   4.

   5.

B. 1. 6   2. 9
   3. 3   4. purple
   5a. likely   b. never

C. 1. 2   2. 3
   3. 5   4. 13
   5.   6.

   7.

D. 1. fewer ; 33   2. more ; 35
   3. more ; 28

Science

A. 1. food   2. warmth
   3. water   4. air

B.

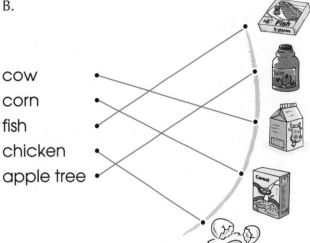

cow
corn
fish
chicken
apple tree

C.

ISBN: 978-1-897457-96-2

ANSWERS

D.

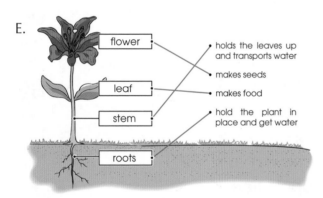

egg ; milk ; bread ; cereal

E.

flower	holds the leaves up and transports water
leaf	makes seeds
stem	makes food
roots	hold the plant in place and get water

Social Studies

A. (Individual answers)
B. (Individual drawing and answers)

Week 3

English

A. 1. at his neighbour's garage sale
   2. one dollar
   3. in his backyard
   4. robins, bluebirds, and cardinals

B. 1. Bob found a treasure.
   2. Bob bought the bird bath.
   3. Bob put the bird bath in the backyard.
   4. He filled the bath with water.
   5. The sun warmed the water.

C. 1. outside   2. backyard
   3. afternoon   4. bluebirds

D. newspaper ; pancake ; mailbox ; goldfish ;
   football ; watermelon ; butterfly ; cupboard

E. 1. A SWALLOW   2. CRACKERS
   3. A BLUEBIRD

Mathematics

A. 1. 23 ; 23 ; B   2. 32 ; 32 ; B

B. 1. 7   2. 4
   3. 10   4. 8
   5. 6 + 6 ; 12 ; 12   6. 7 + 8 ; 15 ; 15

C.

D.

ISBN: 978-1-897457-96-2

E. 1. 2   2. 14
   3. Sunday   4. Thursday
   5. 3   6. 21

Science

A. In the forest: fox ; bear
   In the river: shrimp ; fish
   In the tree: bird ; squirrel

B.

C.

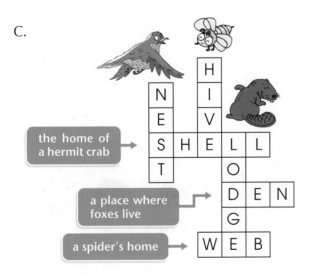

D. 1. egg ; tadpole ; frog
   2. egg ; caterpillar ; chrysalis ; butterfly

Social Studies

A. (Order may vary.)
   1. A ; F ; B ; C ; G ; H ; E ; D
   2. (Individual answer)
   3. (Individual answer)
B. (Individual answers and drawing)

Week 4

English

A. 1. picking   2. baskets
   3. trunk   4. rows
   5. red   6. mouth
   7. sweet
B. (Draw lines through these sentences.)
   1. There was a robin in the sky.
   2. Jan and Ted enjoy riding their bikes with Aunt Mary.
   3. Grapes are purple in colour.
   4. Cherries are red too.
   5. I can make baskets.
C. (Individual drawing and writing)
D. 1. sk ; skates   2. sp ; spider
   3. pl ; plane   4. cl ; clown
   5. fl ; flag   6. gr ; grapes
   7. fl ; flower   8. st ; star

Mathematics

A. A: square   B: triangle
   C: rectangle   D: rectangle
   E: circle   F: triangle
B. square: 3
   triangle: 4
   rectangle: 9
   circle: 5
C. 1.

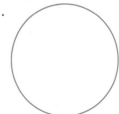

; circle

2.

 ; triangle

3.

 ; rectangle

4.

; square

D. (Individual colouring)

E. 1. longer ; over   2. bigger ; under
   3. right ; bigger   4. A ; B

Science

A. 1. triangle   2. square
   3. circle   4. rectangle
   (Individual drawing)

B.

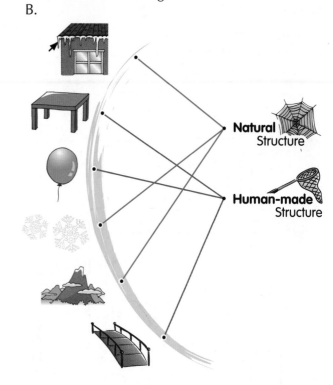

Natural Structure

Human-made Structure

C.

ISBN: 978-1-897457-96-2

D.

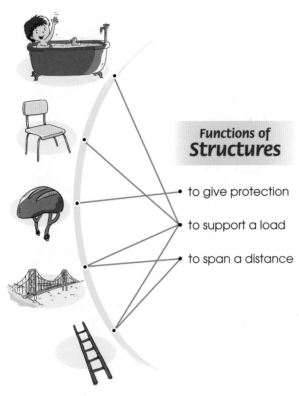

Functions of Structures

- to give protection
- to support a load
- to span a distance

Social Studies

A. 7 ; 3 ; 2 ; 5 ; 4 ; 1 ; 6
B. (Individual answers)
C. (Individual drawing and writing)

Week 5

English

A. Check: 2, 4, 5, 6
B. 1. Check: A, C, D, E, F, H, K, L
   (Suggested answer) sleeping bag
   2. You do not want to get wet inside the tent if it rains.
C. 1. little   2. up
   3. light   4. night
   5. in   6. sad
   7. cold
   8. (Individual writing)

D.

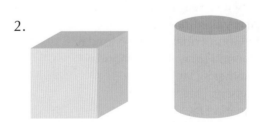

Mathematics

A. 1. sphere   2. cone
   3. cube   4. cylinder
B. D ; C ; B ; A
   A ; B ; D ; C
C. 1. on ; in front of ; beside
   2. inside ; beside ; under
   3. over ; between ; behind
D. 1.

2.

E. Check: C, D

ISBN: 978-1-897457-96-2

F. 1.

bigger

2.

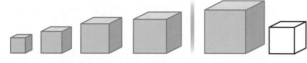

lower

Science

A. iron: B, D
   cloth: E, I
   glass: G, H
   feather: A, F
   wood: C, J
B. F ; F ; F
   S ; S ; S
C. (Individual answers)
D. (Individual examples)
   Things that Need Energy:
   A, C, H, I
   Things that Do Not Need Energy:
   B, D, E, F, G, J
E. 1. grow ; move
   2. change ; think

Social Studies

January: New Year's Day
February: Valentine's Day
March: Good Friday, Easter Monday
April: Good Friday, Easter Monday
May: Mother's Day
June: Father's Day
July: Canada Day
August: Civic Holiday
September: Labour Day
October: Thanksgiving Day
November: Remembrance Day
December: Christmas Day, Boxing Day

Week 6

English

A. Check: 3, 4, 5
B. (Cross out these sentences.)
   1. The red wagon was in the garage.
   2. The feathers were very soft.
   3. Her father works at a bank.
C. 1. start - begin ; hard - difficult ;
      weeping - crying ; sad - unhappy ;
      quick - fast
   2. The baby was crying.
   3. It was difficult to pedal my bicycle up the hill.
   4. We will start the game now!
   5. Sharon is sad to see her friend leave.
   6. That is a fast skunk!
D. 1. PUP   2. EYE
   3. BIB   4. NOON
   5. DAD   6. MOM

Mathematics

A. 1. never
   2a.    2b.

   3. always   4.

B. 1. 13 ;
$$\begin{array}{r} 6 \\ + 7 \\ \hline 1\,3 \end{array}$$

   2. 12 ;
$$\begin{array}{r} 4 \\ + 8 \\ \hline 1\,2 \end{array}$$

   3. 7 ;
$$\begin{array}{r} 1\,6 \\ - 9 \\ \hline 7 \end{array}$$

ISBN: 978-1-897457-96-2

4. 8 ;

$$\begin{array}{r} 1\ 5 \\ -\quad 7 \\ \hline 8 \end{array}$$

C. tigers: 3 ; giraffes: 50 ;
   raccoons: 42 ; geese: 79
D. 1. 46 ; 50 ; 52 ; 56
   2. 45 ; 50 ; 60
E. 1. circle ; 4   2. triangle ; 2
   3. square ; 3   4. rectangle ; 3

Science

A.

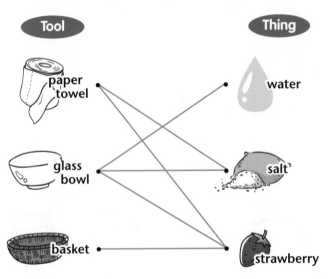

B. Solid: cheese ; sugar ; flour
   Liquid: oil ; milk ; juice
C. 1. solid ; Check: hat, comb
   2. liquid ; Check: water, coffee

D.

E. 1. liquid ; solid
      freezes ; ice
   2. solid ; liquid
      melts ; water

Social Studies

A. 1. hospital   2. school
   3. fire hall   4. library
   5. zoo   6. park
B. 1. C   2. A
   3. D   4. B
   5. nurse   6. mail carrier
   7. teacher

ISBN: 978-1-897457-96-2

Week 7

English

A. 1. small → large
   2. jumping → flying
   3. backpack → seat
   4. sky → ground
B. 1. in her family car
   2. to Calgary
   3. cousin Josie
   4. a flight attendant
C. 1. Sabrina left Toronto on an airplane.
   2. She landed in Calgary, Alberta at 11:00 a.m.
   3. Her cousin Josie met her at the airport.
   4. I flew to Halifax with my friend Peter.
D.

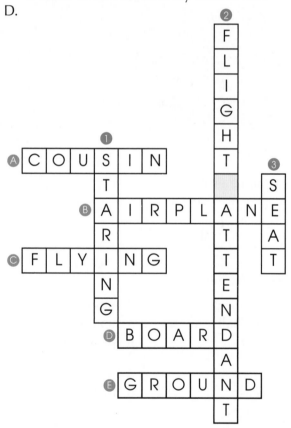

E. (Individual writing)

Mathematics

A.

B. pail: A ; tank: A ; bathtub: C ; bowl: B
C. 1a. 7   b. 5
   2a. pail   b. jug
   3. 2   4. 2
D. 1. a bottle
   2a. 5   b. 12
   3. (Suggested answer) a tank
E.

ISBN: 978-1-897457-96-2

Science

A. Daily Meals:

Times of the Day:

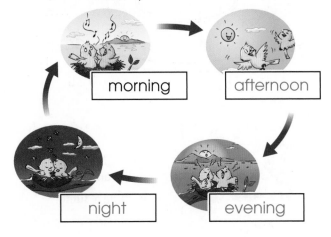

B. light ; spins ; daytime ; nighttime ; hours ; cycle

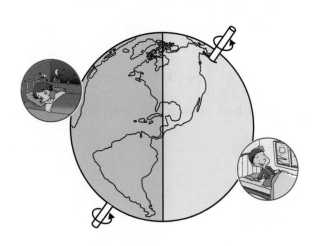

C.

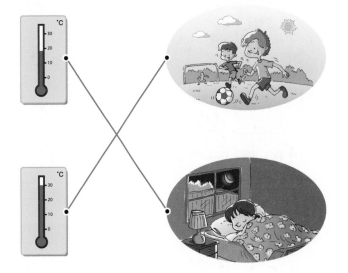

D.

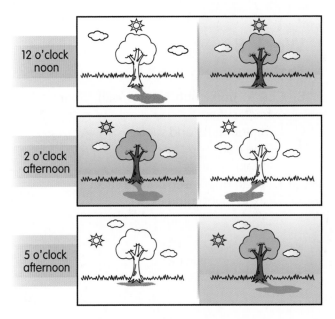

ISBN: 978-1-897457-96-2

Social Studies

A.

(Individual answer)

B. 1. ☺   2. ☺

3. ☺   4. ☹

5. ☹   6. ☺

Week 8

English

B. Check: milk, butter, eggs, salt, flour, vanilla extract, sugar

C. 1. butter, milk, and sugar
2. one hour
3. cookie cutters
4. on an ungreased cookie sheet
5. six to eight minutes

D. (Individual colouring)

E. 1.

"I can be a pet."
"I have fur."
"I bark."
"I have a tail."
"I chase mice."
"I purr."

2. they can be pets, they have fur, and they have a tail.
3. dogs bark but cats purr, and cats chase mice.

ISBN: 978-1-897457-96-2

Mathematics

A. 1. 4   2. 6
   3. 3   4. 8
   5.

   6.

B. 10 ; 4 ; half past 6 ; 8 o'clock
   Events in Order: 4 ; 3 ; 1 ; 2

C. 1. 3   2. 1
   3. 2   4. 10
   5. 19   6. 4
   7. 13   8. 5

D. 1.

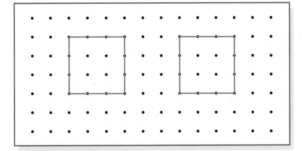

square

2.

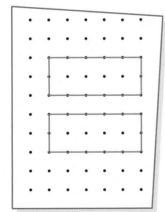

rectangle

3.

triangle

Science

A. 1. fall

2. summer

ISBN: 978-1-897457-96-2

3. winter

4. spring

Social Studies

A.

B. Check: A, B, E
1. Clean   2. rice
3. tape

B. spring: B ; summer: A ; fall: B ; winter: A
(Individual answer and writing)

C. 1. A: winter ; B: spring ; C: summer ; D: fall
2. A: fall ; B: summer ; C: spring ; D: winter

D. 1. sun   2. year
3. seasonal   4. summer

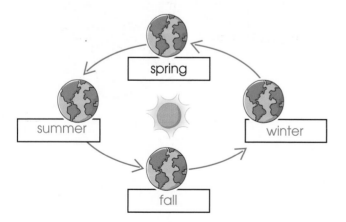

ISBN: 978-1-897457-96-2

Colour the letters and cut each page along the dotted lines. Then staple the pages in alphabetical order to make a little animal book.

This book belongs to

_____

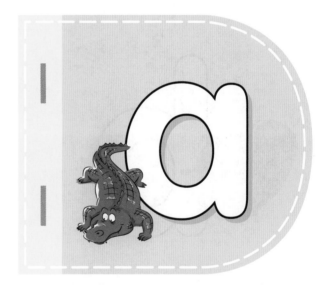

ISBN: 978-1-897457-96-2

Grade 1-2

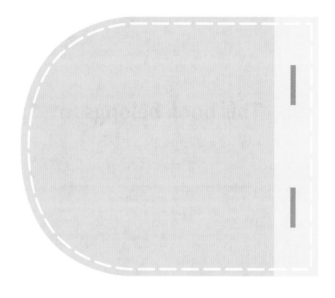

ISBN: 978-1-897457-96-2

ISBN: 978-1-897457-96-2

ISBN: 978-1-897457-96-2

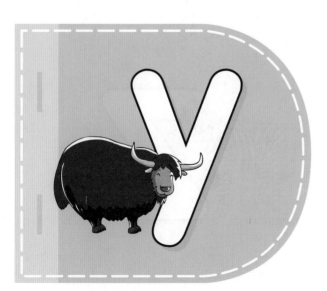

195

ISBN: 978-1-897457-96-2

Grade 1-2

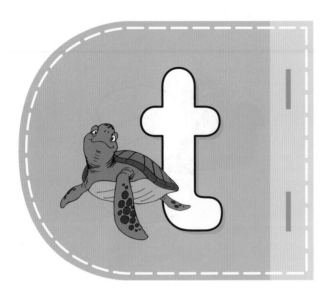

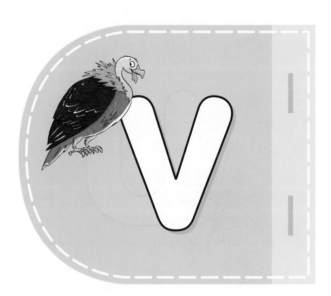

ISBN: 978-1-897457-96-2

A Bingo Game

Trace the letters on the four bingo boards. Then cut out all the boards and the letter pieces on page 199 as well. Put the letters face down. Take turns to draw a letter and show it. Then cross out the picture with that letter.

The first one to cross out the whole row or column of pictures and say "Bingo" is the winner.

For 2 to 4 players

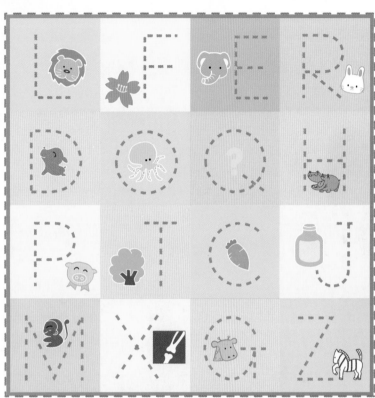

ISBN: 978-1-897457-96-2

Grade 1-2

ISBN: 978-1-897457-96-2

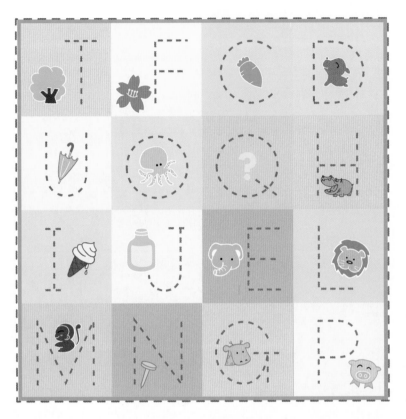

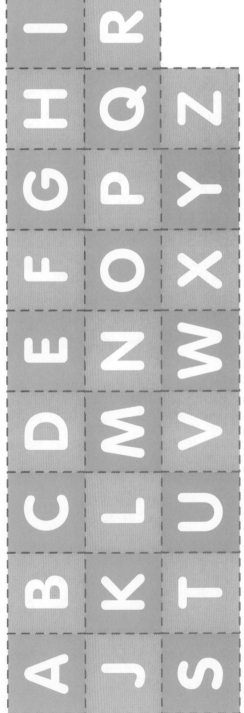

ISBN: 978-1-897457-96-2

ISBN: 978-1-897457-96-2

Tangram Fun

Cut out the tangram. You can use the pieces to form the things shown on this page or make your own pictures.

ISBN: 978-1-897457-96-2

Grade 1-2

ISBN: 978-1-897457-96-2

My Mini-box

Write your name. Trace the shapes on the box to complete the pattern. Then cut out the net and glue the tabs.

> Cut out the things you like and put them into your mini-box.

_____'s Box

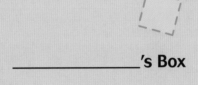

Glue

Glue

Glue

Glue

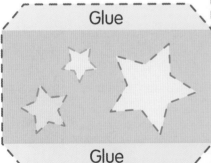

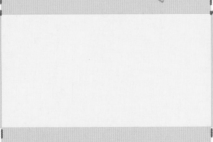

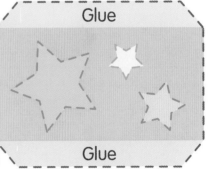

ISBN: 978-1-897457-96-2

Grade 1-2

ISBN: 978-1-897457-96-2

Follow the steps to make a beautiful flower.

1. Cut out A.
2. Calculate and find the petals with the answers.
3. Cut out the petals.
4. Glue the petals onto the correct places on A.
5. Cut out B.
6. Glue B onto A.
7. Done.

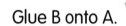

Glue B onto A.

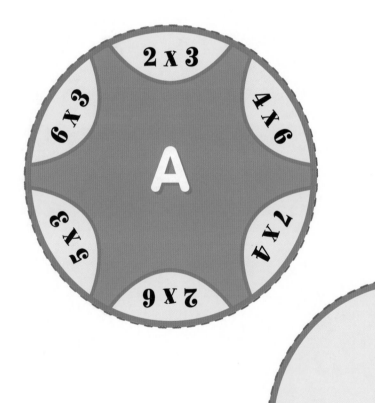

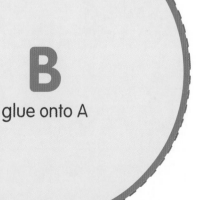

ISBN: 978-1-897457-96-2

Grade 1-2

ISBN: 978-1-897457-96-2

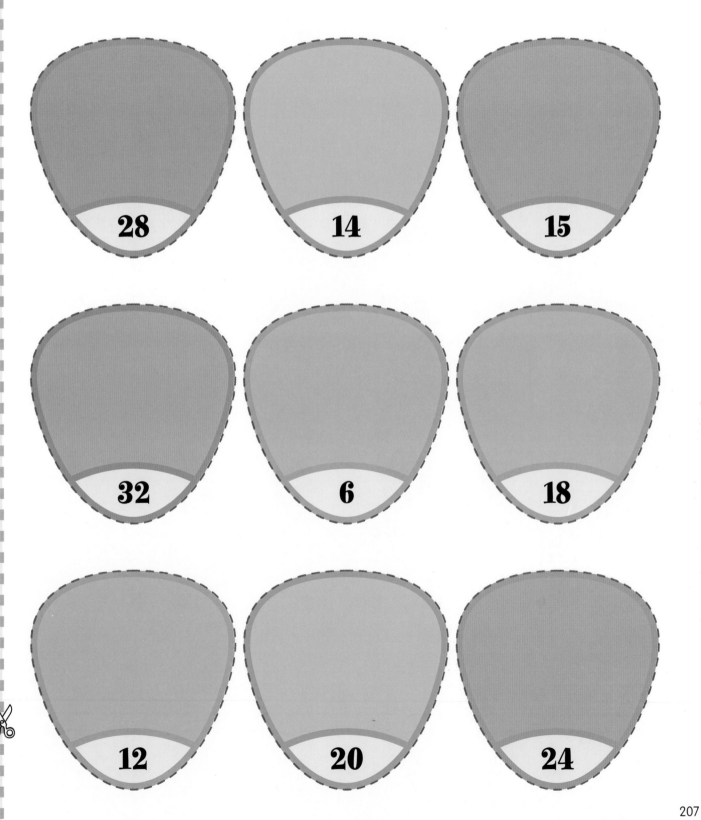

28

14

15

32

6

18

12

20

24

ISBN: 978-1-897457-96-2

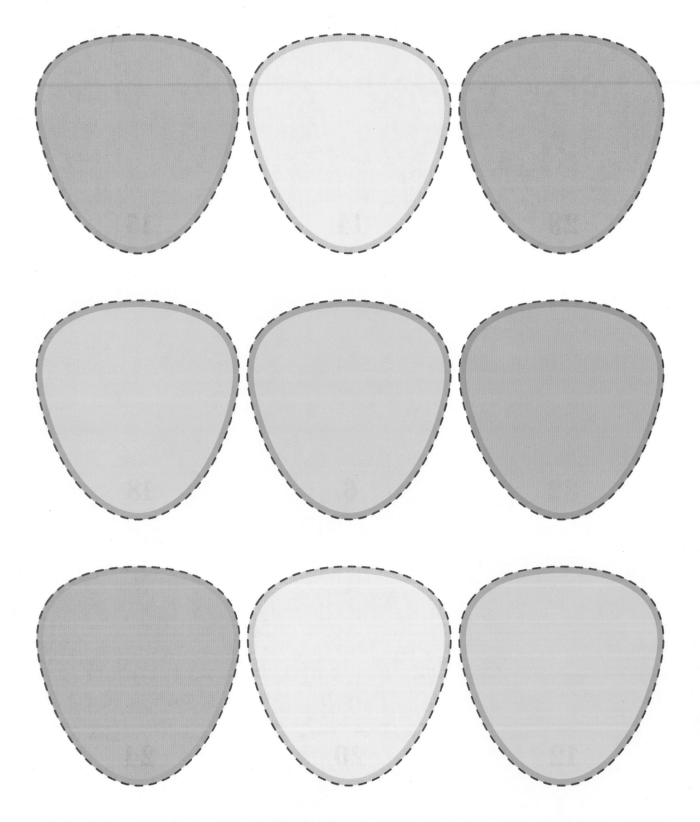

ISBN: 978-1-897457-96-2